THE NATURAL HISTORY PUZZLE BOOK

This edition published in 2019
by Carlton Books Ltd
20 Mortimer Street
London W1T 3JW

Text and design © 2019 Carlton Books Ltd
Artworks and photographs © 2019 The
Natural History Museum

10 8 6 4 2 1 3 5 7 9

A CIP catalogue for this book is available
from the British Library.

ISBN 978-1-78739-326-4

Printed in Dubai

Dr Gareth Moore would like to thank
Laura Jayne Ayres for her assistance with
researching and writing this book.

NATURAL
HISTORY
MUSEUM

THE
NATURAL HISTORY
PUZZLE
BOOK

Dr Gareth Moore

CARLTON
BOOKS

CONTENTS

INTRODUCTION

The universe is a mind-boggling 13.8 billion years old, while our planet, Earth, is a relatively youthful 4.5 billion years old. A lot has happened in that time – the Earth cooled and slowly formed into a habitable environment, life took root and very slowly evolved from single-celled organisms into the incredibly complex entities you see every day, and finally, around 200,000 years ago *Homo sapiens* first appeared.

Since humans first began to reason and wonder, we have been exploring the world in order to understand it better. The Natural History Museum, London, is just one of many institutions working together around the globe to further our knowledge of everything around us, from the earliest beginnings of our planet, to the furthest reaches of Space.

The Natural History Puzzle Book explores our understanding of the world with the help of something else that has been around for thousands of years - puzzles! The earliest puzzle that we have identified was written over 4,000 years ago, and it's likely that early humans were using puzzles and games to entertain themselves even longer ago than that.

Every puzzle in this book relates to an aspect of our scientific knowledge, from the structure of DNA and human evolution, to the symmetry of butterflies and the movement of tectonic plates. Above the title of each puzzle you will see one or more hexagons. These relate to the difficulty of the puzzle on that page. A single hexagon means that the puzzle should be solvable by any member of the family, with a bit of hard-thinking and perseverance! Three hexagons means that an adult might be needed to help to get to the correct solution.

Whether you are a puzzle expert or not, this book can be enjoyed by everyone. With colourful images and interesting facts throughout, this is the perfect puzzle book for any budding young scientist!

DIFFICULTY LEVEL

⬡ EASY

⬡⬡ MEDIUM

⬡⬡⬡ HARD

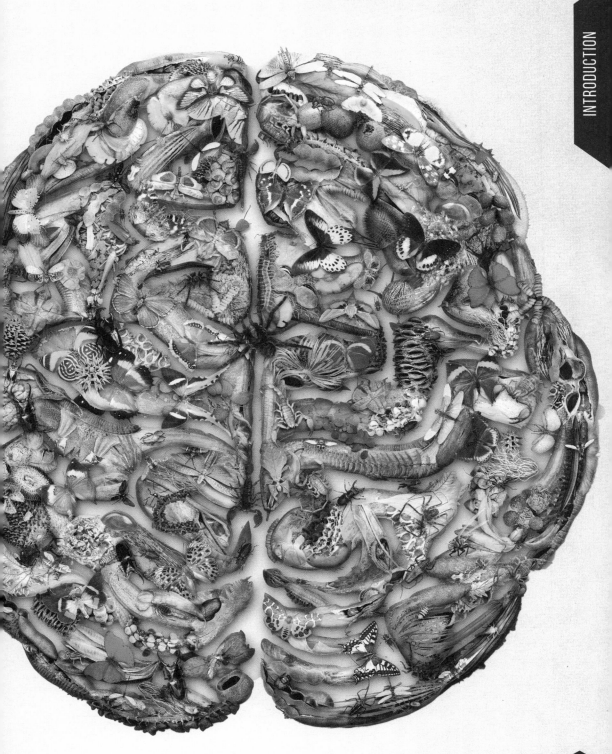

CHAPTER 1:
ANIMALS

THE ANIMAL KINGDOM

What do you, me, a lobster and a polar bear all have in common? We're all animals! Animals can be found all over the globe – in the seas, skies and on land. Some of them are already familiar to us – you might even keep one as a pet – but Earth is home to some truly weird and wonderful creatures.

Scientists who study animals are known as zoologists. To make it easier to understand the animal kingdom, zoologists classified animals into two main groups with other animals that share similar features: vertebrates and

Common Binomials

Can you draw lines to match the common name for each animal with its Latin binomial name? And then can you find the binomial names in the wordsearch?

COMMON NAME	BINOMIAL NAME
ARCTIC HARE	BISON BISON
ASIAN ELEPHANT	BOS TAURUS
ATLANTIC SALMON	CANIS LUPUS
BARN OWL	DANAUS PLEXIPPUS
BISON	ELEPHAS MAXIMUS
CAT	EQUUS FERUS
COW	FELIS CATUS
GIANT CLAM	HOMO SAPIENS
GREY WOLF	LAMA GLAMA
HUMAN	LEPUS ARCTICUS
LION	LYNX LYNX
LLAMA	PANTHERA LEO
LYNX	SALMO SALAR
MONARCH BUTTERFLY	TRIDACNA GIGAS
POLAR BEAR	TYTO ALBA
WILD HORSE	URSUS MARITIMUS

invertebrates. Animals in the vertebrates group all have backbones, and despite making up only 3% of the world's species, you'll find all the mammals, fish, birds, reptiles and amphibians in this group. Invertebrates, on the other hand, have no backbone at all, and come in all shapes and sizes, from tiny ants to giant squid.

All living things are assigned a Latin name, made up of two parts, called a **binomial.**

Can you find the binomial names in the wordsearch?

```
E L E P U S A R C T I C U S I
H L X M N S A L M O S A L A R
O E E F C O A M A L G A M A L
M S Q P E A S A D S S I N L O
O U X U H L N I B S U I S R E
S R R N U A I I B L E M G R L
A U C E Y S S S N A Y A Y A
P A M E M L F M C L O O O U R
I T E T E A X E A A U S T S E
E S U A N U Y N R X T P I Y H
N O O X E B I N Y U I U U B T
S B A A N C I A E L S M S S N
U R S U S M A R I T I M U S A
T R I D A C N A G I G A S S P
D A N A U S P L E X I P P U S
```

MATCHING ANTLERS

Antlers grow on various species of the deer family, including moose, reindeer and elk. Typically, they grow in symmetrical pairs and are re-grown every year. Can you match the pairs of antlers below?

DID YOU KNOW?

Reindeer (also known as caribou in North America) are one of the only species where both males and females grow antlers.

No Gnashers

Most mammals have teeth of some kind, but anteaters don't have any. Instead, they have long, sticky tongues for scooping up lots of tiny insects in a single lick.

PRIMATE LIVING

Chimpanzees live in social groups, sometimes of up to 150 individuals. Not all of them always get along, however, and some groups can be extremely territorial.

Each group in the following chimpanzee area contains six different family members, represented by a different chimpanzee. Can you draw lines to divide this area up into regions so that each region contains one of each different chimpanzee?

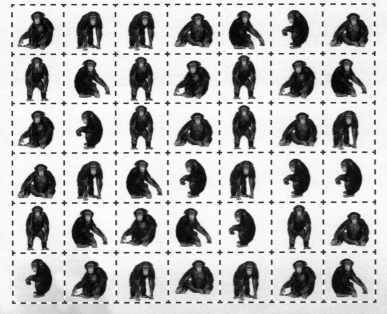

ANIMALS

DID YOU KNOW?

Humans are primates too! Our closest living relative is the chimpanzee.

Noisy Neighbours!
The howler monkey can be heard from over three miles away, even in thick rainforest.

THE WATERING HOLE

The word **"hippopotamus"** comes from the Greek for **"water horse"**. They are mammals but spend much of their time underwater cooling off – so it's less of a surprise that their closest living relatives are **whales!**

In the picture above, you can see different animals that have all gathered at the water's edge for a drink. Spend a minute or two trying to memorize where all the animals are, then cover it up. Then, in the second picture below, see if you can remember where each animal was. Draw a line to their original position around the watering hole.

LARGE ANIMALS

A large animal is hiding in this picture. Can you reveal it by solving the clues? The clues provide, in reading order, the length of every run of consecutive shaded squares in each row and column. There must be a gap of at least one empty square between each run of shaded squares in the same row or column.

DID YOU KNOW?

Elephants can use their trunks as snorkels when they're swimming underwater.

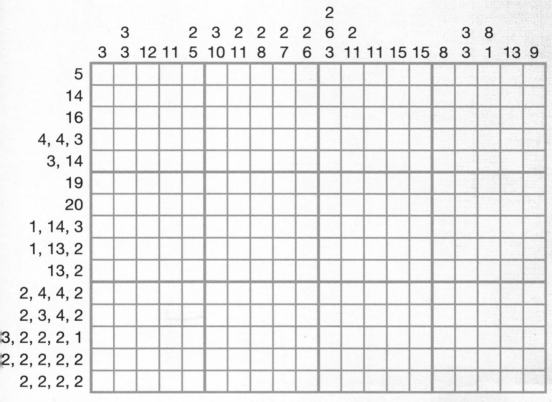

Column clues (top):

	3				2	3	2	2	2	2	6	2				3	8		
3	3	12	11	5	10	11	8	7	6	3	11	11	15	15	8	3	1	13	9

Row clues (left):

- 5
- 14
- 16
- 4, 4, 3
- 3, 14
- 19
- 20
- 1, 14, 3
- 1, 13, 2
- 13, 2
- 2, 4, 4, 2
- 2, 3, 4, 2
- 3, 2, 2, 2, 1
- 2, 2, 2, 2, 2
- 2, 2, 2, 2

FIND THE SNAKE

DID YOU KNOW?

A Tight Squeeze
The world's largest
snakes aren't venomous.
Anacondas, pythons and
boa constrictors instead
have strong muscles
that they use to squeeze
their prey until they
fall unconscious.

Shade in some of the squares below to reveal a single
snake, starting at the head (H) and ending with the
tip of the tail (T) that is already included in the grid.
Numbers outside the grid specify the number of
squares in their row or column that contain part of
the snake.

The snake is a single path of adjacent shaded squares
that does not branch. Shaded squares cannot touch,
except for the immediately preceding and following
squares in the snake. Shaded squares also cannot
touch diagonally, except when necessary for the
snake to turn a corner. Besssssst of luck!

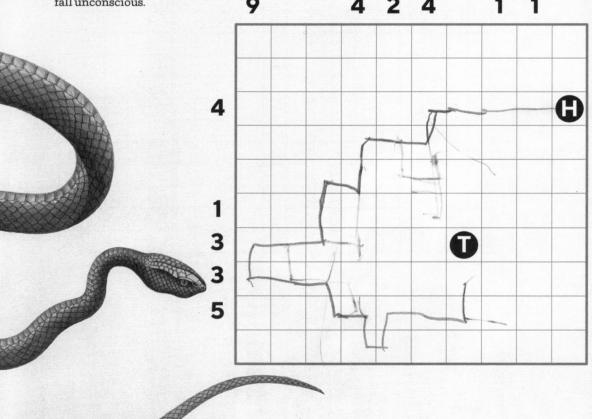

A SQUARE DISGUISE

Colour each of the squares below according to the number key to reveal a hidden image.

What can you see? And can you then find another of the same type of animal somewhere else in this book?

Living Dragons?
Did you know that there's a group of lizards called Draco *which are also known as flying lizards? They use their "wings" to glide from tall trees, and their name comes from the Latin word for "dragon".*

Key: 1 = blue **2** = black **3** = pale blue **4** = dark green **5** = light green **6** = orange
7 = green **8** = yellow **9** = red **0** = dark red **A** = brown **B** = dark brown

FLIGHT OF THE BUMBLEBEE

ANIMALS

Bees tell their fellow bees the best routes to the best flowers through the medium of dance. Well, to be precise, they do it by wiggling their behinds in various patterns.

By looking at the bees positioned around the compass, who are showing you four different wiggles, can you follow this bee's directions to the nearest flowers to collect some pollen for the hive?

CLUE
Use these 20 wiggles to plot your route on the grid - one wiggle per square, starting on the hive and finishing on the flower.

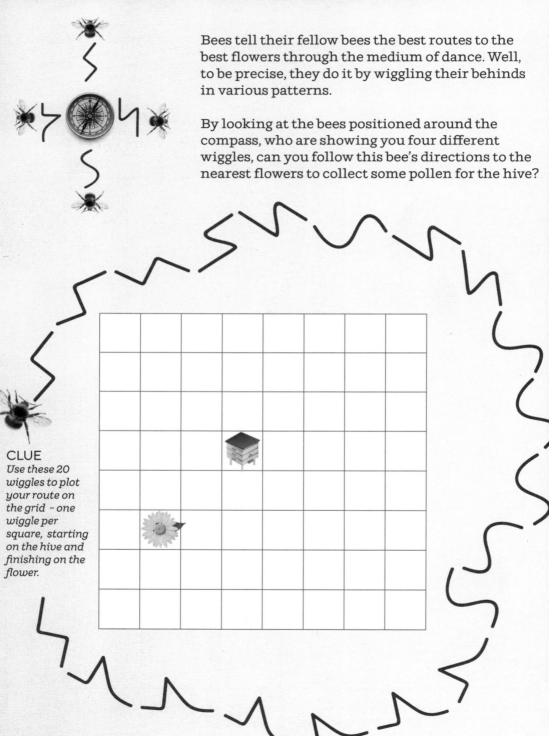

BUTTERFLY BIAS

Butterfly wings are almost always symmetrical, but can you spot ten differences (in total) on the left and right wings of the three butterflies below?

BEAUTIFUL BEETLES

Here are 24 beetle specimens. Prove that you are a budding entomologist (someone who studies insects) by matching them up into 12 identical pairs.

DID YOU KNOW?

A **beetle** has two pairs of wings. The front pair are hardened into wing-cases, called *elytra*, distinguishing them from most other insects.

1 IN 4

Beetles are the largest group of living organisms in the world. In fact, it is estimated that one in every four animals in the world is a beetle!

12 identical pairs?

mandible

foreleg

palp

antenna

mid leg

elytra

hind leg

PENGUIN PAIRS

Penguins mate for life and take turns hunting for food while they're looking after their young. Penguin colonies can be huge, however, so it can take a while to find their partners again when they come back from fishing. Reunite the penguins below by drawing a path to join each penguin to its identical mate. Each square can only have one path going through it, and the paths must never cross – don't let the penguins get mixed up!

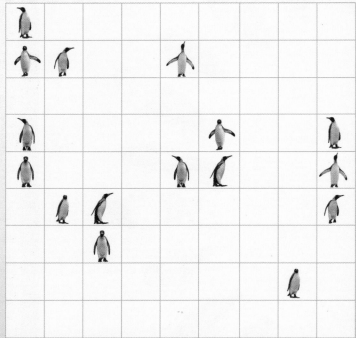

SPLIT EGGS

These eggs have fallen from a nest and broken in half. Can you match the two halves of each of these eggs to make them whole again?

That's Not My Chick!

Cuckoos lay their eggs in the nests of other birds and then leave them there to be brought up by an unwitting "foster" mother. When the cuckoo chick hatches, it pushes the other chicks out of the nest so it can keep all of the food for itself.

BIRDWATCHER'S PARADISE

Birds of paradise
are members of a
family found mainly in
Indonesia, Papua New
Guinea and Australia.
The males have much
brighter, more colourful
feathers than the
females.

Can you build yourself a great birdwatching hideout by building bridges between the tall trees of the rainforest? Each of the circles in the puzzle below represents a tree, and the numbers inside tell you exactly how many bridges must connect to each tree. Draw bridges either horizontally or vertically from tree to tree to make a network across the treetops, making sure that bridges don't cross either one another or over trees. Once done, you must be able to travel from any tree to any other by using bridges. No more than one bridge can join any pair of trees.

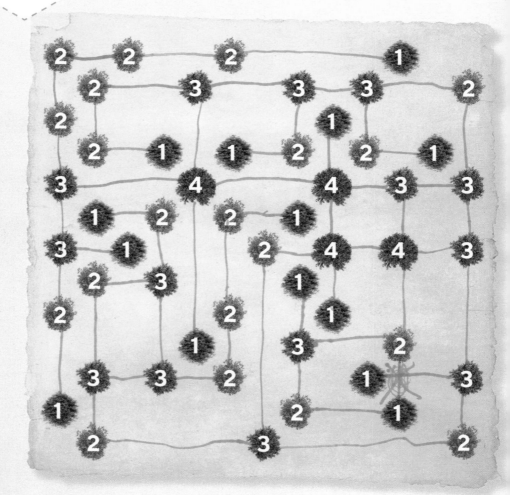

FEATHERED FACTS

Use the following facts to answer the mathematical questions beneath:

- The wandering albatross has the largest wingspan of any living bird, growing to 3.5m (11 $\frac{1}{2}$ft).
- Ostriches weigh as much as 145kg (320lbs) - heavier than any other bird.
- An ostrich egg weighs roughly 2% of its mother's body weight.
- The lightest bird is the bee hummingbird, weighing less than 2g ($\frac{7}{100}$oz).
- Hummingbirds have extremely fast heartbeats - up to 1,250 beats per minute - and take an average of 250 breaths every minute.

? If you were 175cm (5ft 9in) tall, then how many times bigger might a wandering albatross's wingspan be than your arm span? (Your own personal arm span will be almost the same as your height).

? Roughly how many times heavier can an ostrich be relative to a bee hummingbird? And for a bonus point, why do you think it's called a bee hummingbird?

? If an 80kg (176lbs) ostrich laid an egg, how much would the egg weigh? And how many times heavier would the egg be than a bee hummingbird?

? Roughly how many breaths does a hummingbird take in an hour?

DID YOU KNOW?

The largest bird that ever lived (around 10 million years ago) had a 5m (16.5ft) wingspan.

*Not all parrots live in tropical areas. There is a species of parrot called the **kea**, which is the world's only alpine parrot. It can only be found on South Island, New Zealand.*

JUNGLE COLOUR

Use the number key below to colour in the mystery amphibian, found in the rainforests of Central and South America. When you're done, take a look at the colours you've used and see if you can guess what its name is.

Key:

1 = light green
2 = green
3 = dark green
4 = light blue
5 = pink
6 = purple
7 = orange
8 = light brown
9 = brown
0 = dark brown
A = light grey
B = dark grey
C = red

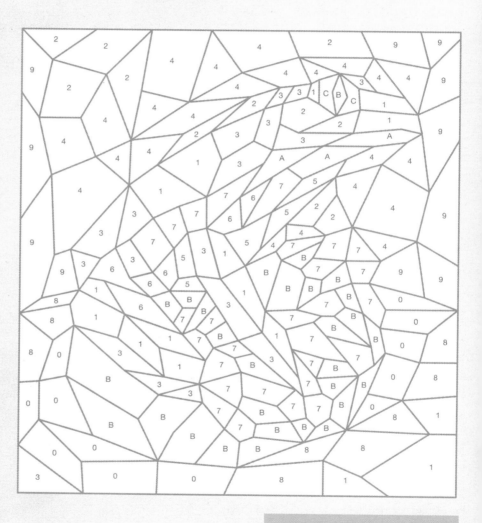

A Breath Of Fresh Air

Many amphibians breathe through their skin by a process called "cutaneous respiration". As a result, some species, such as some salamanders, don't even have lungs!

LIFE CYCLE OF FROGS

Frogs aren't born looking like frogs. They start off as eggs, which then grow long tails to become tadpoles, then they eventually lose their tails and grow into adult frogs. Those adults lay more eggs in turn, continuing the life cycle.

In the grid below, can you place each of the three stages of a frog's life cycle - an egg, a tadpole and a frog - so that each appears exactly once in every row and column? The pictures around the outside of the grid show you which of the three stages is encountered first in that row or column, reading inwards from the picture. Two squares in each row and column will remain empty.

Two Ways To Live
Amphibians can live in water and on land at different stages of their life, which is how they get their name. "Amphibian" derives from the Greek for "both lives".

The Australian frog **Cyclorana platycephala**, *known as the water-holding frog, spends most of its time burrowed underground to keep itself cool.*

NIGHT-TIME CREATURES

Have a look at the image below of a tropical forest at night. How many animals can you spot?

Bats make up around 20% of all mammal species.

Many bats find their way in the dark using echolocation: they send out a noise signal and wait for it to bounce back. The longer it takes for the sound to echo, the further away an object is.

Pangolins *are nocturnal mammals – and the only ones to have scales on their skin. They use them to roll into an armoured ball when threatened.*

HIDDEN ANIMALS

Human eyes aren't well adapted to seeing in the dark, unlike those of nocturnal animals.

This puzzle requires you to work out where some animals might be, even when you can't see them. Instead, number clues are given, where each number reveals the exact count of how many creatures are found in its touching squares, including diagonally touching squares. No more than one animal can be found in a single square, and animals aren't found in squares which contain numbers.

Owls *have huge eyes to help them see in the dark - but they're so big they can't move them. They turn their heads when they need to look in a new direction.*

A small number of animals are members of the **marsupial** *group, only found in Australia and the Americas. The females have a pouch in which they raise their young.*

		3			3	2
	6			6		
		4				
	4			4		2
					2	
2		2	4	2		
	2				2	1

NIGHT-TIME MYSTERY

Can you tell what's out there? Join the dots in increasing numerical order to reveal a nocturnal animal from the Southern Hemisphere. When you reach a number with a hollow star, lift your pen and start again at the next number, which will have a solid star.

HABITAT MATCH-UP

Animals have adapted to live in very different types of climate, from the freezing North Pole to the scorching Sahara Desert.

See if you can match the habitats below with the animal you're most likely to find living in them.

HABITAT	ANIMAL
AMAZON RAINFOREST	BAT
ANTARCTIC	BLUE POISON DART FROG
CAVE	HEDGEHOG
DEEP OCEAN	HERMIT CRAB
DESERT	PENGUIN
ROCK POOL	SCORPION
SAVANNAH	VAMPIRE SQUID
WOODLAND	ZEBRA

*The snake **Crotalus cerastes**, known as the sidewinder, has developed the unusual technique of moving sideways. This makes it easier to travel on the sand of its native north and central American deserts.*

*The **Atacama Desert** in South America is one of the driest places on earth, with an average of 15mm (½in) of rain per year. Sometimes, four years can pass without any rainfall at all.*

▼

PENGUIN PROTECTION

Polar bears and penguins never meet in nature, since polar bears live in the Arctic, while penguins are only found in Antarctica and other places in the Southern Hemisphere.

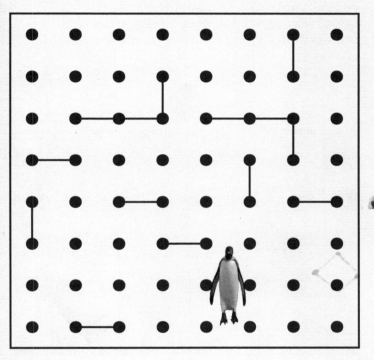

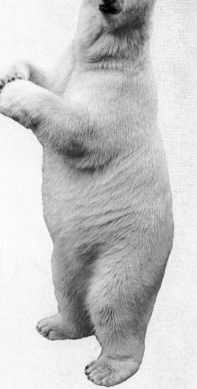

In a zoo, however, they can often be found closer together. So, can you draw a fence to join all of these fence posts in order to protect the penguin from the nearby polar bear?

The fence should form a loop that visits every post exactly once, without crossing over or touching itself at any point. Only horizonal and vertical lines can be drawn between fence posts (dots), since the fence is constructed from fixed-size panels.

HIDDEN IN PLAIN SIGHT

Some animals are masters of disguise, and can be almost impossible to spot unless they are moving.

Test your own ability to see through camouflage by finding the following pattern in this grid of coloured squares. You must find it in the given orientation - that is, not rotated or reflected in any way.

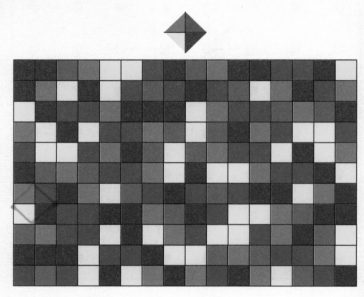

The smallest species of chameleon is **Brookesia micra** *- it's so small it could sit comfortably on matchstick!*

Do you recognise this animal from the answer to page 17? **Chameleons** *don't always change colour to disguise themselves. They sometimes use their colour-changing abilities to communicate with other chameleons, or to help control their body temperature.*

SPIDER'S WEB

Spider's webs can be hard to see, which makes them great for trapping insects.

Insects are all members of the order *Diptera*, from the Greek for "two wings". See if you can find **DIPTERA** in the following web of letters, by starting on any "D" and then follow lines to adjoining letters in order to spell out the word.

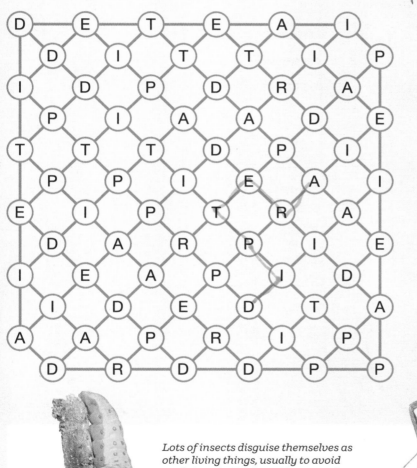

*Lots of insects disguise themselves as other living things, usually to avoid predators. A stick insect is one such master of disguise, but did you know there is a type of butterfly common in the USA, **Papilio troilus**, which is disguised to look just like a snake when in its larval form?*

ANIMAL ORDERINGS

Can you order these animals from 1 to 5 based on their weights?

Write a number next to each animal to show its relative weight, with 1 being the heaviest animal and 5 being the least heavy.

- Polar bear
- Emu
- African bush elephant
- Blue whale
- Hippopotamus

Can you order these animals from 1 to 5 based on how endangered they are?

Write a number next to each animal, with 1 being the most endangered and 5 being the least.

- Chimpanzee
- Bottlenose dolphin
- Great white shark
- Jaguar
- Javan rhino

TEST YOUR KNOWLEDGE

? **Which of these animals can move the fastest?**
a) Peregrine falcon
b) Cheetah
c) Black marlin
d) Greyhound

? **Only one of these birds can fly. Which one?**
a) Cassowary
b) Kiwi
c) Condor
d) Emu

? **What is a "diurnal" animal?**
a) An animal that eats only insects.
b) An animal that sleeps at night and is awake during the day.
c) A striped animal.
d) An animal which lives underground.

? **True or False?**
When caught by a predator, some
lizards can choose to lose their tail
and leave it behind to give them
a chance to escape.

*Many animals are endangered because of
human behaviour. For example, deforestation
means that* **orangutans** *are being forced out
of their natural environment and now struggle
to survive.*

SPREADING OUT ANIMALS

The six animals below are all examples of endangered species, with efforts being made around the world to increase their numbers in the wild.

Place them into the grid, spreading them out so that exactly one of each animal appears in every row and column - but also making sure that two of the same animal don't touch each other, not even diagonally. Some are already given.

*Illegal poaching is a huge threat to many animals. One species of rhino was declared **extinct** in 2011 after years of being killed for its horn.*

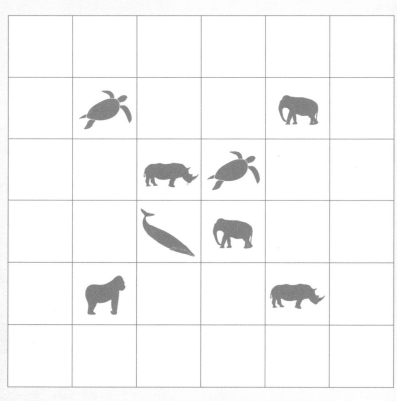

GREEN TURTLE

TIGER

BLUE WHALE

GORILLA

RHINO

ASIAN ELEPHANT

ONE OF A KIND

Many animals that were once plentiful are now extremely rare. Can you place just two Amur leopards into every row, column and fenced-off region of this puzzle? The leopards can't be in touching squares, including diagonally touching squares.

Meet **Hope**, *the blue whale that hangs in the Natural History Museum, London. Blue whales were hunted to the brink of extinction in the twentieth century, but were also one of the first species that humans decided to save on a global scale.*

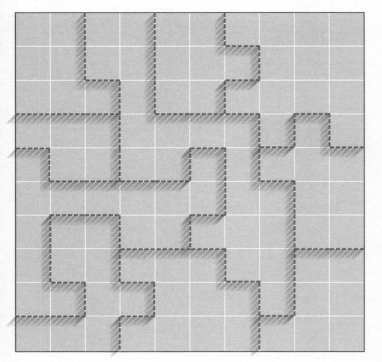

The **Amur leopard** *is the most endangered of all the leopard species - there are less than a hundred that survive in the wild.*

DIG AND DISCOVER

For animals that became extinct long ago, we only learn of their existence once their bones or fossils are discovered. Can you unscramble the anagrams below to uncover the names of some extinct animals? Only the letters are important – the spacing may not correspond with that in the original name.

DID YOU KNOW?

Extinction happens when the last animal of its kind dies. The most familiar extinct animal is probably the **dodo**, a large flightless bird that lived on the island of Mauritius.

1. O ODD

2. TO MY HOLLOW MAM

3. TINY LEACH

4. KITCHEN BARRELS NOW

5. TO LONG-DEAD

6. MY OLD NO

7. AQUA GG

8. SOLO MIND

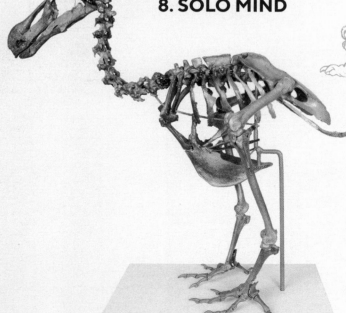

FOSSIL HUNT

Can you find your way through
this maze to a remote site where
some exciting fossils have just
been discovered?

CHAPTER 2:
OCEANS

OCEANS

There are five oceans on the planet that, added together, cover about 70% of the surface of Earth. The largest ocean is the Pacific, followed by the Atlantic, Indian, Southern and Arctic - and they all link together to form one giant body of water, known as the World Ocean.

Under the surface, there's a whole host of marine life to discover, in environments that range from bright, colourful coral reefs to the dark depths of the ocean floor. The ocean floor is lined with volcanoes, mountains and deep trenches, and - as you'll see on the following pages - even underwater forests.

In fact, 95% of the ocean is still unexplored - so there's still more out there to discover! About 20,000 species were discovered in just the past decade alone, and scientists estimate there are still half a million new species waiting to be found. But the oceans, and the living things that call it home, are under threat - global warming, overfishing and pollution are all threatening this huge range of species.

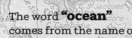

DID YOU KNOW?

The word **"ocean"** comes from the name of the Greek god Oceanus, who was believed to be the human embodiment of the sea.

CAPTAIN JAMES COOK.

PAINTED BY N. DANCE ESQ^R R.A.

PRESENTED TO GREENWICH HOSPITAL BY THE EXECUTORS OF

SIR JOSEPH BANKS, BART. K.B.

THE OPEN OCEAN

Below are the names of some marine explorers and details of their greatest achievements.

Can you find their names in the wordsearch?

JAMES COOK - *Cartographer and explorer who created the first precise map of the Pacific Ocean.*

ERNEST SHACKLETON - *Arctic explorer, most famous for his survival after his ship Endurance was wrecked.*

SYLVIA EARLE - *Set the record for the deepest dive without a tether.*

JAMES CAMERON - *First solo explorer of the Mariana Trench - the deepest trench on Earth, much deeper than Mount Everest is tall.*

JACQUES COUSTEAU – *Developed the first aqualung and popularised marine biology.*

VAGN EKMAN - *Developed theories to explain ocean currents.*

JACQUES PICCARD - *Underwater vehicle pioneer and one of the first deep ocean explorers.*

ROBERT BALLARD - *Discovered the wreck of the Titanic.*

FERDINAND MAGELLAN - *An explorer who gave the Pacific Ocean its name.*

MATTHEW MAURY - *Published the first book about oceanography.*

```
U N R T S E J E L C I S T U E
N A A O Y E K R E M A Y Y S D
O L E M B A R O M C N L E R R
T L D T K E T N O T E V Y E E
E E N R S E R H B C R I E M O
L G L O A U N T T A S A T L E
K A O P R C O G B A R E S U E
C M C O M E C C A A E A M M N
A D S P L C M I S V L R R A D
H N N N T R C A P E M L N R J
S A L N R O K H C S U E A V S
T N M R P A T E E S E Q E R K
S I T M A O O L I E E U A Y D
E D L S C Q W J N E O M Q J A
N R M S E S T N A E E D A A E
R E A E T S R E I U C K T J J
E F D M A T T H E W M A U R Y
```

A KELP-ING HAND

DID YOU KNOW?

It might look like giant plants, but **kelp** is actually a type of algae – which belongs to a different scientific family.

The ocean hides huge underwater forests, made of towering columns of a large, brown seaweed called kelp. These provide underwater habitats for all kinds of marine creatures, from jellyfish through to brittle stars. But they can come under threat from sea urchins, who move in huge numbers and can eat their way through the kelp's holdfast, which is what anchors it down to the ocean floor. The urchins themselves have predators, however, such as giant sea otters. They feed on sea urchins and can stop them destroying a whole forest, so they're an important protector of these vibrant habitats.

Can you get through the kelp maze and reach the sea urchin to save the forest from being eaten?

A TALL TALE

You've been provided with a map of a giant kelp forest, but it's been given to you in an unusual format. Instead of recording the height of each piece of kelp, the map shows how many pieces of kelp can be seen from different points around the outside.

Can you write the numbers 1 to 5 into each row and each column, to show the height of each piece of kelp? 1 is the shortest, and 5 is the tallest. Numbers reveal how many pieces of kelp can be seen when looking along their row or column, given that higher pieces of kelp always obscure all shorter pieces of kelp in the same row or column. One piece of kelp is already placed, to get you going.

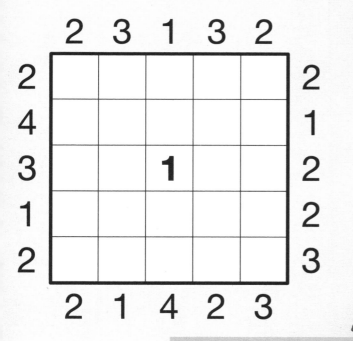

Giant kelp, *a kelp species commonly found in the Pacific Ocean, keeps itself standing upright with the help of gas bubbles that keep fronds afloat on the surface of the water. It can also grow up to 50m (164 ft) tall!*

THE WORLD OCEAN

PACIFIC OCEAN

Test your ocean explorer knowledge!
Can you draw a line between the
name of the sea or ocean and its
location on the world map?

ARCTIC OCEAN

INDIAN OCEAN

SEA OF OKHOTSK

Mind The Gap. *The
Southern Ocean is the name
for the body of water which
surrounds the continent of
Antarctica, and is sometimes
also known as the Antarctic
Ocean. It was formed about
30 million years ago when
the tip of South America and
Antarctica broke apart and
started to allow currents to
move through the gap.*

BERING SEA

NORTH SEA

SOUTH CHINA SEA

SOUTHERN OCEAN

SEA OF JAPAN

BALTIC SEA

A PEACEFUL PLACE

The Pacific Ocean was named by the explorer Ferdinand Magellan, who called it the Mar Pacífico. *Translated from Spanish, it means "peaceful sea".*

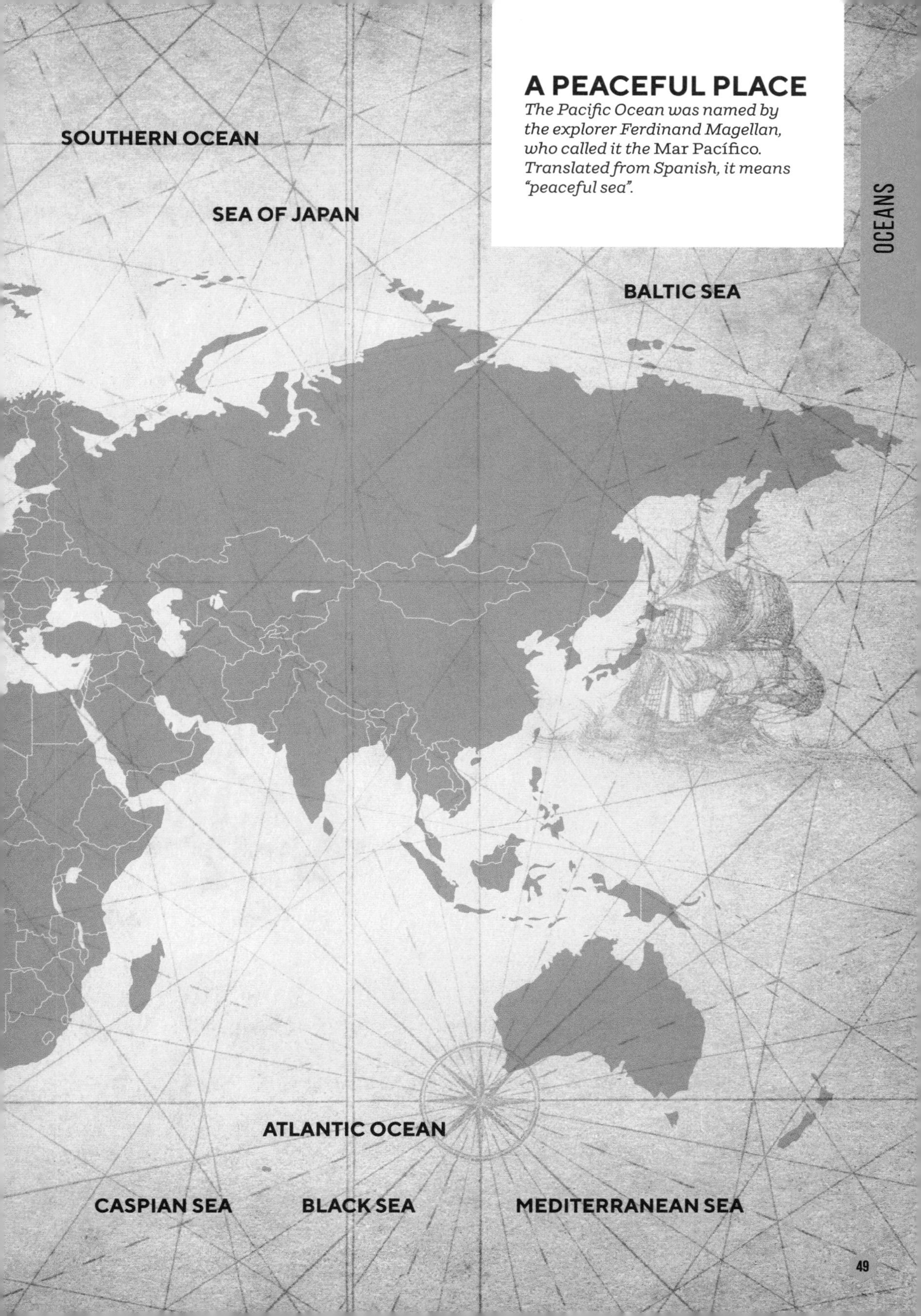

ATLANTIC OCEAN

CASPIAN SEA   BLACK SEA   MEDITERRANEAN SEA

IN A SPIN

It's not just the tide that makes the water move. Currents in the oceans are continually flowing, powered by wind and temperature changes.

The name for an ocean current that moves in a circular shape is a gyre. Sometimes debris and pollution get trapped in gyres and are pushed towards the same location. One area in particular, situated between Hawaii and North America, is known as "The Great Pacific Garbage Patch". It is a large area of the Pacific Ocean where plastic and other rubbish has been collecting together for many years.

Can you create a gyre of your own?
Enter the numbers 1, 2, and 3 into some (not all) of the squares to the right, so that as you trace your way around the spiral from the outside in, you read 1, 2, 3, 1, 2, 3, etc. Each number must appear exactly once in each row and column.

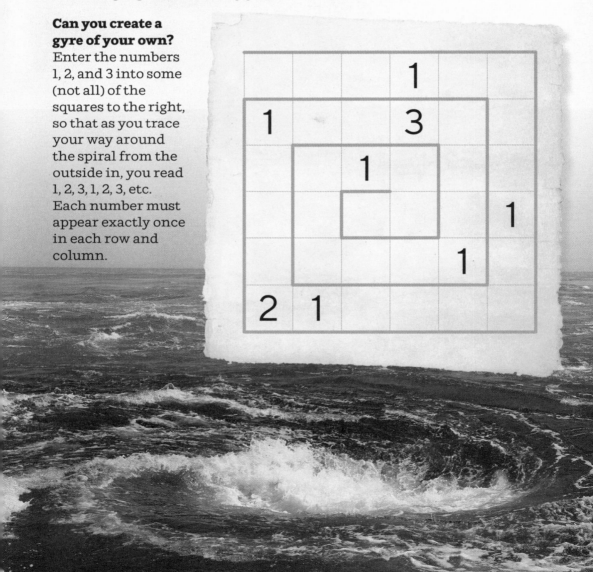

CHANGING DIRECTIONS

Ocean currents are also affected by the Earth's rotation, because it makes the wind move in curved patterns, and then the wind acts on the ocean.

See if you can track the flow of a complex wind pattern in the puzzle below. Number the boxes from 1 to 25, so that every box points directly at the next highest number, therefore forming a path all the way from 1 up to 25. Only one number can be placed per box.

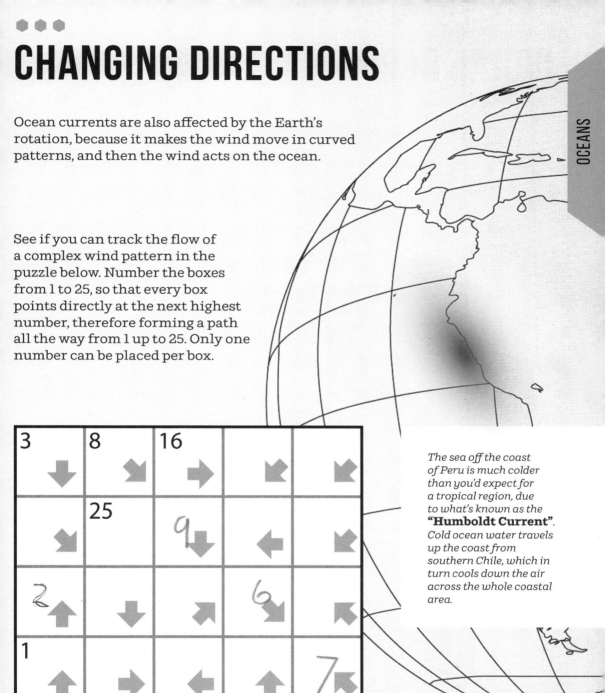

The sea off the coast of Peru is much colder than you'd expect for a tropical region, due to what's known as the **"Humboldt Current"**. *Cold ocean water travels up the coast from southern Chile, which in turn cools down the air across the whole coastal area.*

CORAL REEFS

Living Reefs

Coral reefs may look like they are built on rock, but they are actually a bone-like skeleton built up by the many tiny coral animals that live on it. Reef-building corals have hard outer skeletons, and when they group together to form a reef, it creates large, super-strong structures where other animals can build their homes. Over time it grows larger and larger, as the animals build on top of the existing skeleton.

Home Sweet Home

Coral reefs form protective homes for many different animals. They grow in different shapes and sizes, creating underwater mazes for fish to explore.

Can you explore the maze-like reef below and find your way to the centre of this coral structure?

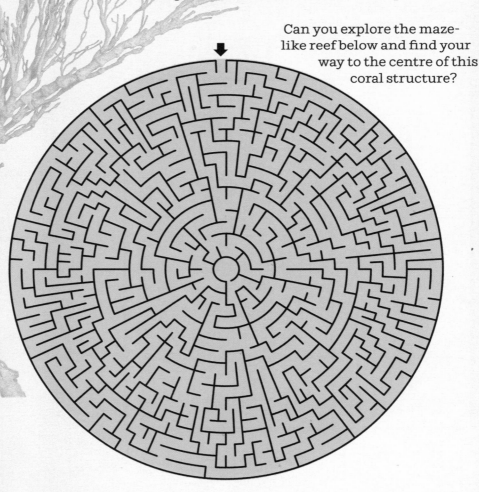

TEMPERATURE TROUBLE

Many of the world's coral reefs are under threat from global warming as rising sea temperatures kill coral, leaving behind just the white skeletons. This is known as coral bleaching. Coral can sometimes recover after bleaching, however, if they become habitable again.

See if you can complete the temperature measurements in the area of sea below by placing a digit from 1 to 9 in each empty square, so that no number repeats in any row, column or bold-lined 3x3 box. Digits placed on the thermometers must increase in value from the bulb to the head of each thermometer, so every digit along the length of the thermometer must be greater than all of the digits before it.

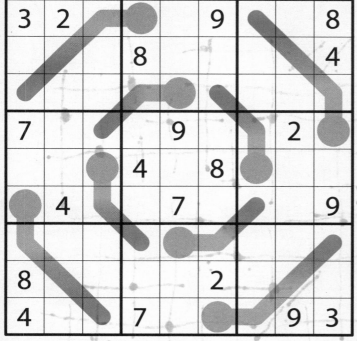

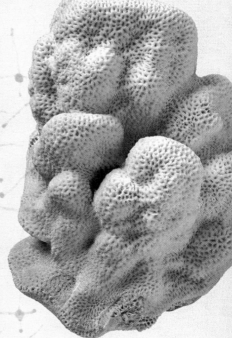

LIGHT UP THE DEEP

Sunlight doesn't reach very far beneath the surface of the water, so in the deeper parts of the ocean the fish and other marine animals sometimes make their own light to find their way – and find their prey! The creation of light by living things is known as "bioluminescence".

See if you can light up the puzzle below by adding your own lamps to it, according these rules:

- You can add a lamp to any empty square, but not a black one.

- Light shines out of every lamp in both horizontal and vertical directions along the same row and column. Light travels until it reaches either the edge of the grid or a black square.

- Some black squares have numbers on them. This exact number of lamps must be placed in the touching squares (left/right/up/down)) – no more, and no less.

- Every light square must be lit by at least one lamp.

- No lamp can shine on any other lamp.

*Bioluminescence isn't just found in the deep ocean. In some warmer climates, tiny marine plants and animals called **plankton** can be seen glowing in the dark on the surface of the ocean, making waves appear to light up as they crash on the shore.*

Can you think of an **insect** *that uses bioluminescence?*

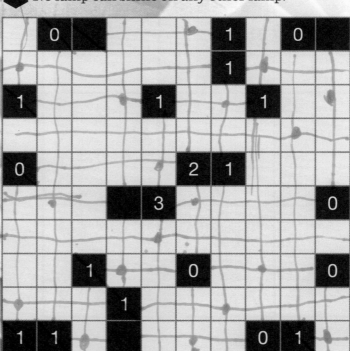

QUITE A CATCH

Lurking in the grid below is a deep-sea predator. Colour the squares according to the number grid to reveal what's hiding in the dark.

Key:
1 = dark blue
2 = black
3 = dark green
4 = green
5 = light blue
6 = yellow
7 = white

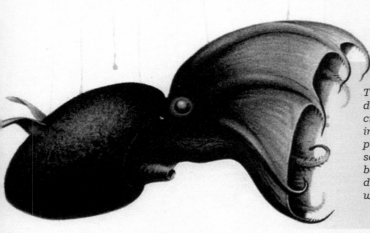

*The **vampire squid** lives in the deep ocean and has the ability to create flashing lights on its skin in order to confuse and startle predators. It's called the vampire squid because the webbed skin between its tentacles looks like a dark cloak. It's not something you'd want to bump into in the dark!*

DEEP-SEA LIFE

When pressured sea water bursts through super-hot volcanic rocks on the ocean floor, it creates a deep-sea vent called a "black smoker". The water in the vent is rich in minerals from Earth's crust, and the warm, mineral-rich areas around deep-sea vents are very attractive to life. One creature sometimes found near them is the giant tube worm, which can grow up 2.5m (8ft) in length!

In the puzzle below, draw your own tube worms by connecting matching (same colour) heads and tails together with a body that travels horizontally and vertically from the head to the tail. Only one body can enter any square, and bodies cannot cross.

It's tempting to imagine the ocean floor as being flat sand, but in fact there are mountain ranges, volcanoes and deep underwater trenches – just like on Earth's surface. One well-known underwater mountain range is the **Mid-Atlantic Ridge**, *found at the bottom of the Atlantic Ocean.*

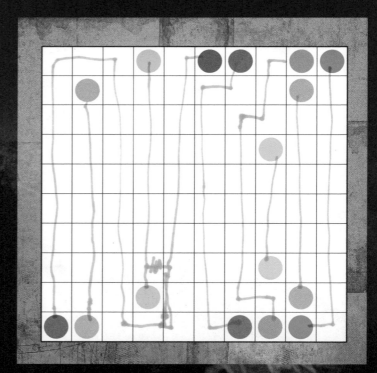

Did you know there's such a thing as an underwater waterfall? It sounds impossible, but they do exist! In areas where hot and cold water meet along an ocean mountain range, the hot water rises towards the surface and the cold water plunges downwards, creating a waterfall effect along the edge of the rock.

5
5
1
5
3
5
6

3 6 6 3 3 5 4

In the puzzle to the left, shade some squares so that they contain water. All water in a connected area must pool as it would in real life, so water must fill an area from bottom to top, not from top to bottom. Water does not flow through bold-lined walls, however. Numbers outside the grid reveal how many squares contain water in each row and column.

The world's largest waterfall is underwater, and is known as the **Denmark Strait Cataract**. *You could find it between Iceland and Greenland - if you were 610m (2,000ft) beneath the surface!*

EVERY DAY'S A SHOAL DAY

Have a look at the two pictures below and see if you can spot ten differences between them. Look closely - this is a shoal of fish, so some fish might have changed direction, or even swum away entirely!

School or shoal?

It's often said that "school" is the name for any group of fish, but "schooling" means something quite specific in marine biology. If a group of fish is schooling, it means they're moving together in a tight and unified formation, all swimming in the same direction at the same time - like herring do. Shoaling, on the other hand, happens when a group of fish swim together in a social way, sometimes straying from the group and swimming at their own pace.

Gentle Giants

The oceans cover most of Earth's surface, so it's not surprising that some of the largest animals in the world are found underwater. The largest fish is the whale shark - which is very docile, despite being a shark, and feeds mainly on plankton. It can reach 19m (62ft) in length.

The **giant oceanic manta ray**, found mainly in tropical areas, can grow to over 8m (26ft) across - that's almost the length of a double-decker bus!

A MIGHTY MOSAIC

The oceans contain many mighty predators. Can you find the tell-tale signs of a well-known example in the puzzle below?

Shade some of the squares so that each number is surrounded by the given number of shaded squares – left, right, up, down and diagonally, as well as the numbered square itself.

A TASTY TREAT

Some species of **pufferfish** are highly prized edible fish, but they have to be very carefully prepared by well-trained chefs. They are so toxic that, when the wrong parts are eaten, they can be fatal to humans.

Jumping Jaws!
The goblin shark, which lives in the deep-sea zone, has jaws which jump out towards its prey when hunting.

0								0	0		2	4	
		0		0		0	1	2			6	6	
0			0			1	3		5		7	6	
	0		0		1		5		5		6	4	2
		0		0	1	3	5		3	4		3	
	0			1			3	1	3	4			
			3	5					3				
	0					3			3		3		0
	0		4	5	4		0		0	3	3	3	0
			4	4	2	0		0			4	1	
		3	4	4	1			0			5	3	1
1		4	5		3	3	3	2		3	6	7	6
3	5	6						5				8	
5		8			9			8	8	8			
								6			6		4

Not all marine creatures are put off by venom or stings. One **hammerhead shark**, which preys on stingrays, was found with 96 venomous barbs in its mouth!

ANEMONE, NO ENEMY

The fish in the picture below has come up with a clever way of hiding from predators - by making its home inside sea anemones on coral reefs. The anemones have stinging tentacles, which discourages other fish from coming near.

Colour in the picture according to the number key to find out who's hiding in the anemone.

NOT A ROCK

Stonefish are so well disguised that they are sometimes stepped on by swimmers or divers who mistake them for actual rocks. They are the most venomous fish in the world, and their venom can be fatal.

Key:
1 = blue
2 = dark blue
3 = black
4 = green
5 = dark green
6 = light orange
7 = orange
blank = leave white

Not all fish have spikes and venom to protect them from predators. The **mandarin dragonet** is covered in a sticky mucus which has a horrible taste, designed to stop anyone trying to eat it. It sounds disgusting, but it's also one of the most colourful fish in the ocean.

GO FISH

Below are the jumbled-up names of some fish you might have read about in this chapter – and some you might already know.

Can you unscramble them?
Ignore any spaces, which are not part of the answer.

1. AUNT

2. PAIRS FORTH

3. SHE AROSE

4. IF REPS HUFF

5. HALF SINGER

6. OFTEN HISS

7. SHIRK LOG BAN

8. SPIKED RUMP

*Some fish have unusual adaptations to their surroundings, which make them seem almost not like fish at all. For example, **mudskippers** are known as "amphibious" fish because they can survive outside of water for hours – or sometimes even days.*

A COURTLY DANCE

Seahorses perform a courting dance in pairs before mating. Each dance has many different steps, and it might continue for up to five days. Tiring!

Can you match the identical pairs of seahorses so that they are all partnered up?

HOLD ON TIGHT!

The **Connemara clingfish** is equipped with a powerful sucking device to help it cling on to rocks, and stop it from being swept away by strong tides.

*A **seahorse** is a fish, although its hard outer protection means it's not a very fast swimmer. The females deposit their eggs into a special pouch on the male, so it is the male seahorses who actually "give birth" - sometimes to thousands of babies at once.*

A WHALE OF A TIME

You can tell how old a sperm whale is by looking at its teeth. For every year of the whale's life, a ridge is formed inside its tooth, a bit like how a tree trunk grows rings every year.

Count the ridges and see if you can tell how old this sperm whale was.

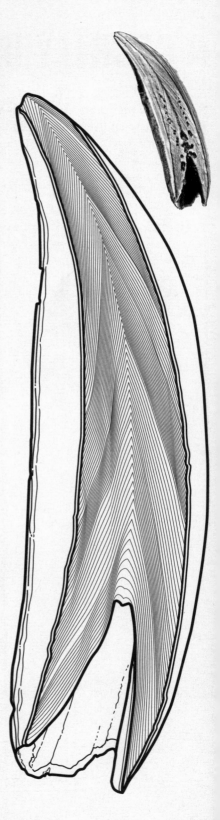

The **blue whale** is one of the loudest animals on the planet, and its calls can be heard up to 500 miles (805km) away.

The **blue whale** is the largest living animal on Earth - and possibly the largest animal that has ever lived. They were hunted almost to extinction in the twentieth century, but numbers are now growing in the wild. Despite its enormous size, the blue whale eats only small creatures that it sucks up as it swims along.

CRACK THE CODE

Dolphins are highly intelligent and communicate with each other underwater using a series of clicks and whistles. They even create individual sounds for themselves that they use to identify one another.

Imagine that two dolphins have been heard talking to each other, and a marine biologist has come up with a way to record each word using a series of dots and dashes, which match up to the sounds made by the dolphins. Using the guide below, can you crack the code and work out what one dolphin said to the other?

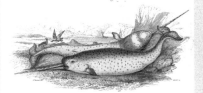

The **narwhal** is sometimes called the "unicorn of the sea" because of the long "tusk" which grows out of its head. They are found in the cold waters of the Arctic Ocean, and are closely related to beluga whales.

HERE'S THE KEY:

A ·--	HAVE ·-·	SHALL --·
ARE ·	I -	STRIPES ·-·
DIVING --·	LUNCH --·	SWIMMING ···
GOING ---	RACE ·-	WE --

AND HERE'S WHAT THE DOLPHIN SAID:
BLEEP BLIP   BLEEP BLEEP
BLIP BLEEP BLIP
BLIP BLEEP BLEEP
BLIP BLIP BLIP
BLIP BLEEP

CRUSTACEANS

Try these number-based crustacean puzzles. "Crustacean" is a general name for animals such as crabs, lobsters, shrimps and barnacles.

Most crustaceans have hard outer exoskeletons, which they shed many times in a lifetime to grow bigger ones. In fact, a lobster can grow a new shell as many as 40 times a year in its first year of life.

Crustacean Equations

? If a hermit crab had to replace its shell every three months, how many different shells would it require over four years?

? Krill are tiny crustaceans, but they're the food of choice for the world's largest animal - the blue whale - which can eat up to 40 million krill in one day. If one krill is 5cm (2in) long, how many could line up end-to-end to equal the length of a 25m (83$\frac{1}{3}$ft)-long blue whale?

? Giant isopods (below left) and common woodlice (below right) are very closely related and look similar - except that the latter lives on land, and the former in the deep ocean. There's a big size difference too - a giant isopod can weigh 1.7kg and grow up to 75cm long. If a common woodlouse is 15mm long, how many times longer is a giant isopod?

SHELLECTION TIME

Have a look at the shells below and see if you can spot one that is different from the others.

DID YOU KNOW?

Every **shell** that you find on the sea shore used to be part of a living animal - and sometimes still is! Most of them are made by bivalves, a group of marine molluscs.

*When a **hermit crab** grows, it has to find a new shell it can move into. Sometimes, whole groups of crabs line up from largest to smallest so they can all upgrade their homes at the same time, making sure none of them is left vulnerable without a shell.*

HIDE AND SNEAK

DO YOU KNOW?

Squid, octopus and cuttlefish all belong to a group of molluscs called **cephalopods**. Cephalopods can swim backwards, squirting large jets of water to propel them along. The nautilus also belongs to this group and is the only cephalopod to have a shell.

Some sea invertebrates are masters of disguise. The animal in the picture below can change colour to imitate the rocks and corals around it, camouflaging itself to hide from predators.

Join the dots in increasing numerical order to reveal this highly intelligent and well-disguised invertebrate! When you reach a hollow star, lift your pen and start again at the next number, which will have a solid star.

SHADY SEA-CREATURE

Shade some squares in the grid below to reveal a creature which very few scientists have managed to lay eyes on in the wild, despite its huge size. It lives in the deep ocean and has enormous eyes that help it to see in the low light conditions – the biggest eyes in the animal kingdom, in fact.

The clues provide, in reading order, the length of every run of consecutive shaded squares in each row and column. There must be a gap of at least one empty square between each run of shaded squares in the same row or column.

	2	3	2	2	3	5				1			2	2			2	1	1	
	2	2	3	2	2	2	4			2	2		3	4	1	2	7	6	6	
	2	2	3	2	2	2	4		2	1	2	4	2	2	6	10	2	3	3	5
	2	3	3	3	3	2	4	12	4	1	7	7	1	3	6	5	3	2	1	3
4																				
2, 2, 1																				
3, 3, 2																				
4, 2, 4																				
3, 2, 6																				
3, 1, 6																				
3, 3, 9																				
19																				
7, 6																				
1, 2, 3																				
6, 2, 2, 1																				
8, 2, 1																				
3, 3, 4																				
15																				
2, 2, 2, 2, 3																				
2, 2, 2, 3, 2																				
3, 2, 2, 2																				
3, 2, 2, 3																				
3, 2, 2, 3																				
2, 2, 3, 4																				

Cuttlefish *can communicate with other cuttlefish by changing the colour and texture of their skin, even giving themselves brightly coloured stripes like a zebra. They can change colour very quickly – in less than a second!*

AN ARM AND A LEG

The **giant sunflower starfish** *can grow up to 1m across - that's a big starfish!*

Brittle stars are closely related to starfish. They are both echinoderms, just like sea urchins and sea cucumbers. Brittle stars have long and flexible arms which they can choose to lose if they are being hunted and need to make a quick escape.

Can you match the lost arms below with the brittle star that they broke off from?

MIND THE JELLYFISH!

Most jellyfish stings aren't fatal to humans, although they can be very painful. Unfortunately, jellyfish can be very hard to spot while you're in the water, but see if you can help find the hidden jellyfish in the grid below so that you can avoid being stung.

The numbers tell you how many jellyfish there are in the squares touching each numbered square, including diagonally. Shade in where you think the jellyfish are hiding, and remember that there aren't any hiding in the squares with numbers already in. No more than one jellyfish can be found in any single square.

The **Portuguese man o' war** is not actually a jellyfish, but they both belong to a group known as the Cnidarians. Its tentacles can reach up to 50m (164ft) in length, and its sting is strong enough to kill a human being.

				3		2	
4	4				2		3
		2					
4		3		3			
	4		4			3	
2							3
	2		3		2	3	
1		1		2			

EMPTY OCEANS

Overfishing happens when too many of one kind of fish are caught by humans in a short period, meaning that the population can't regenerate itself fast enough. Whole areas of ocean that were once full of fish can suddenly become very underpopulated.

Look closely at the image to the left and spend a minute or two trying to memorise it. Then cover it up and see if you can remember which fish were where by drawing lines from the fish to their position on the picture below. When you're done, uncover the first picture and see how you did!

SPREADING POLLUTION

Pollution comes in all forms, but water pollution can quickly spread around the world, following the currents and tides.

Track the path of various items of pollution, each marked with a number, in the puzzle below. Each item of pollution spreads to the given number of squares, so pollution marked with "2" spreads to 2 squares, for example.

Pollution only spreads horizontally or vertically from the number, in the same row or column, but can spread in all four directions. No more than one type of pollution can spread to any single square, but every square should be filled. One clue is solved already, to show you how it works.

Sometimes, **sea turtles** and dolphins get caught up in fishing nets. When animals are caught by accident in the fishing industry, they are known as "by-catch".

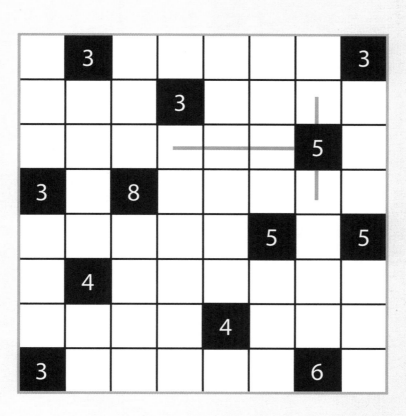

OCEAN DEPTHS

The ocean can be split up into different zones, based on their depth below the surface. These zones all have their own names, which are listed below along with their greatest depth.

Below are some of the marine animals that have appeared in this chapter. Using your best judgement, can you match the animal to the depth zone you'd be most likely to find it in?

ZONES

**EPIPLAGIC
200M**
(656FT)

**MESOPELAGIC
1000M**
(3,281FT)

ANIMALS:

**ANGLERFISH
BOTTLENOSE DOLPHIN
CUTTLEFISH
GIANT SQUID
GIANT TUBE WORM
PORTUGUESE MAN O'WAR
VAMPIRE SQUID
WHALE SHARK**

**BATHYPELAGIC
4000M**
(13,123FT)

**ABYSSOPELAGIC
6000M**
(19,685FT)

OCEAN EXPLORER QUIZ

Attention, ocean explorers! We've visited the deep ocean, coral reef, kelp forest and even an underwater waterfall. But were you paying attention?

Test your ocean knowledge from this chapter by answering the questions in the following quiz:

? What group of invertebrates do squid, cuttlefish and octopuses all belong to?

? How far away can a blue whale's call be heard?

? Which animal's jaws jump out at its prey?

? Can you name the largest crab?

? What length can a Portuguese man o' war's tentacles grow to?

? What kind of animal eats sea urchins and helps protect kelp forests?

? Which is the largest ocean?

? What is the name of the world's tallest underwater waterfall?

? What is the name of the process whereby animals can produce light from their bodies?

? Which is the largest fish in the ocean?

CHAPTER 3:
SPACE

SPACE

Space is silent, since there is no **matter** *for soundwaves to travel through.*

Earth is almost 25,000 miles (40,000km) in circumference at the equator, and the total surface area of Earth is about 200 million square miles (515 million square kilometres). And yet, despite these enormous sizes, Earth is just a tiny speck in our Solar System of eight planets. And the Solar System is a tiny speck in our galaxy, the Milky Way. And that galaxy is just a tiny speck in the universe itself.

Space, then, is vast. So vast that it would take light 225 trillion years to travel from Earth to the edge of the known universe, even though each year that light would travel around 6 trillion miles (9.5 trillion kilometres). These numbers are so large that they are almost impossible to comprehend.

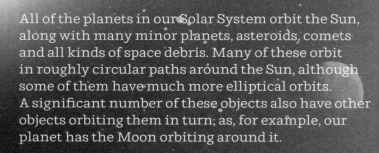

All of the planets in our Solar System orbit the Sun, along with many minor planets, asteroids, comets and all kinds of space debris. Many of these orbit in roughly circular paths around the Sun, although some of them have much more elliptical orbits. A significant number of these objects also have other objects orbiting them in turn; as, for example, our planet has the Moon orbiting around it.

For a long time we have thought of all of the empty space between stars and planets as just that - space. But scientists now suspect it may be full of "dark matter", a strange, invisible substance which we don't yet understand. We think it's there not because we can see it, but because we can see its effects on the things we can measure, such as gravity.

OUTER SPACE

The distances between objects in space are enormous, so finding something in all that emptiness can be tricky. Test out this theory by looking for just one word in this enormous wordsearch.

Can you find the word **SIRIUS**? It's the name of the brightest star in the night sky, also known as the "Dog Star".

There are **more stars** in the universe than there are grains of sand on all the beaches on Earth.

JOURNEY TO THE CENTRE

The universe was created in a massive explosion from a single, tiny point that then expanded to form all of the known universe - the stars, planets and everything else. This expansion continues today, as all of the matter in the universe speeds further and further apart.

Everything in the Milky Way is rotating around a massive black hole at the centre of the galaxy. It has two spiral arms, and our Solar System is on the "Orion" arm. Luckily, we are 25,000 light years from the centre of the galaxy, but can you find your way to the very centre of this circular maze?

The largest known star in the Milky Way, **VY Canis Majoris,** may be as large as 2,000 times the width of the Sun.

THE BIG BANG

Black holes and other massive objects in the universe distort gravity, bending light.

In a similar way - although for a completely different reason - notice how these overlapping circular planets below also bend the square objects placed in front of them. Why do you think this might happen?

The **Big Bang** took place about 13.7 billion years ago.

COLOUR AND UNCOVER

Hidden in the grid below is one of the eight planets from our Solar System. Can you use the number key to colour in the squares and reveal it?

KEY:

1 = yellow
2 = white
3 = black
4 = orange
5 = brown
6 = dark brown
7 = light brown

```
1 2 3 3 3 3 3 3 3 3 3 3 3 3 3 3 3 3 3 3 3 3 3 3 3 3 3 3 3 3 3 3 3 3 3 3 3 3 3 3 3
2 3 3 3 3 3 3 3 3 3 3 3 3 3 3 3 3 3 3 3 3 3 3 3 3 3 3 3 3 3 3 3 3 3 3 3 2 3 3 3 3
3 3 3 3 3 1 1 1 3 3 3 3 3 3 3 3 3 3 3 3 3 3 3 3 3 3 3 3 3 3 3 3 1 2 1 3 3 3 3
3 3 3 3 1 1 1 1 1 1 3 3 3 3 2 3 3 3 3 3 3 3 3 3 3 3 3 3 3 2 2 1 2 2 3 3
3 3 3 1 4 4 4 1 1 1 1 3 3 3 3 3 3 3 3 3 3 3 3 3 3 3 3 1 2 1 3 3 3
3 3 1 4 4 4 1 1 1 4 1 3 3 3 3 3 3 3 3 3 3 3 3 3 3 3 3 2 3 3 3 3
3 3 1 4 1 1 3 1 1 1 1 1 3 3 3 3 3 3 3 3 3 3 3 3 3 3 3 3 3 3 3
3 1 4 1 3 3 3 3 3 1 1 1 1 3 3 3 3 3 3 3 3 3 3 3 3 3 3 3 3 3 3
3 1 4 1 3 3 3 3 3 1 1 4 1 3 3 3 3 3 3 3 3 3 3 3 3 3 3 3 3 3 3
3 1 4 1 3 3 3 3 3 5 5 5 5 5 5 5 5 5 5 5 5 5 3 3 3 3 3 3 3 3 3
3 1 4 1 3 3 3 3 5 5 6 6 5 6 6 7 7 7 7 7 5 5 3 3 3 3 3 3 3 3 3
3 1 1 4 3 3 3 3 5 7 7 6 6 5 6 6 7 6 6 6 7 7 6 5 5 3 3 3 3 2 3
3 1 1 1 1 3 3 5 6 6 7 6 6 5 5 6 6 7 7 7 7 5 3 3 3 3 3 3 3
3 3 1 1 4 4 5 7 7 6 7 7 7 6 6 5 5 5 7 7 7 7 7 6 5 3 3 3 3 3
3 3 1 1 4 1 6 7 7 6 6 7 7 6 6 6 6 5 6 7 7 7 7 7 6 5 3 3 3 3
3 3 1 1 4 4 6 7 7 7 6 6 7 7 6 6 5 6 7 6 6 7 7 7 5 5 3 3 3 3
3 3 1 1 1 4 4 5 5 7 7 7 7 7 6 6 5 6 6 6 6 6 7 7 5 3 3 3 3
3 3 3 1 1 4 4 1 6 5 7 7 7 7 7 6 6 5 5 5 6 6 6 6 7 7 6 5 3 3
3 3 3 1 1 1 1 1 1 5 6 6 7 7 7 6 6 6 6 5 6 6 6 6 6 6 5 3 3
3 3 3 1 1 1 1 1 1 1 6 6 6 6 7 7 7 6 6 5 5 5 5 5 5 6 5 3 3
3 3 5 5 4 4 4 1 1 1 7 5 6 6 6 7 7 7 6 6 6 6 6 6 6 5 5 5 3 3
3 3 5 7 7 1 4 1 1 1 7 5 6 6 6 7 7 7 7 6 7 6 6 6 6 7 5 3 3
3 3 5 7 7 1 1 4 1 4 1 7 5 5 5 6 6 7 7 7 7 7 6 6 7 6 5 3 3
3 3 5 5 6 7 1 1 4 4 7 5 5 5 5 6 6 6 7 6 7 7 7 7 7 5 5 3 3
3 3 3 5 6 6 7 1 4 1 4 7 6 6 6 5 5 6 5 6 6 6 7 7 7 5 5 3 3
3 3 5 6 6 6 4 4 4 4 4 1 6 7 6 5 5 5 5 6 6 6 7 7 5 5 3 3
3 3 5 5 5 5 6 4 4 1 1 1 1 6 7 6 5 5 5 5 6 6 6 7 5 5 3 3
3 3 3 5 6 6 6 5 6 1 1 4 4 6 7 7 5 5 5 5 7 5 5 3 3
3 3 3 5 5 6 6 6 5 6 1 1 4 4 6 7 7 7 7 6 7 7 5 5 5 3 3
3 3 3 3 5 5 6 6 6 5 6 4 1 4 4 4 6 7 7 6 6 7 7 5 5 4 3 3
3 3 3 3 3 5 6 6 6 5 6 4 4 4 4 1 4 1 7 6 6 5 5 5 3 3 4 4 3
3 3 3 3 3 5 5 6 6 5 5 4 4 4 4 4 6 6 5 5 3 3 1 4 1 3
3 3 3 3 3 3 3 5 6 6 5 5 5 1 4 4 4 1 4 1 3 3 1 4 4 4 3
3 3 3 3 3 3 3 5 5 5 5 5 1 1 1 4 4 4 1 1 4 1 1 4 1 3
3 3 3 3 3 3 3 3 3 3 3 3 3 1 3 4 4 4 4 4 4 4 1 4 1 3
3 3 3 3 3 3 3 3 3 3 3 3 3 1 3 4 4 4 1 1 1 1 1 4 1 3
3 3 2 3 3 3 3 3 3 3 3 3 3 3 1 4 4 4 4 1 1 1 1 4 1 3
3 2 1 2 3 3 3 3 3 3 3 3 3 3 3 4 4 4 4 4 4 4 4 3 3
3 3 2 3 3 3 3 3 3 3 3 3 3 3 3 3 4 4 4 3 3 3
3 3 3 3 3 3 3 3 3 3 2 3 3 3 3 3 3 3 3 3 3 2 3
3 3 3 3 3 3 3 3 3 3 3 3 3 3 3 3 3 3 3 3 3 2 1 2
3 3 3 3 3 3 3 3 3 3 3 3 3 3 3 3 3 3 3 3 3 3 2 3
```

A SIZABLE DIFFERENCE

The planets in our Solar System come in very different sizes. The largest one is so big that you could fit over 1,000 planet Earths inside it!

Can you number the planets in the Solar System below in size order, from largest (1) to smallest (8)?

Venus and **Uranus** are the only planets in our Solar System which spin clockwise. All the rest spin anti-clockwise.

Mercury

Venus

Jupiter

Saturn

Earth

Mars

Uranus

Neptune

We used to consider **Pluto** to be a planet, but in 2006 it was reclassified as a dwarf planet. Just like Earth, Pluto has many mountains, although scientists don't yet know how they were formed.

● ● ●

THE BLUE PLANET

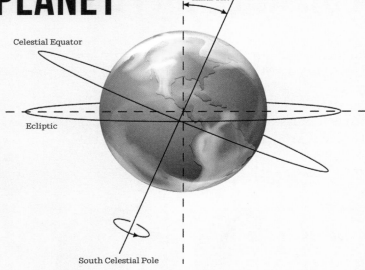

North Celestial Pole

Rotation Axis

Axial Tilt

Celestial Equator

Ecliptic

South Celestial Pole

The Earth rotates at an axis of 23.5 degrees, which is why we have different seasons as it orbits around the Sun. Reveal a picture of our blue planet - more than 70% of it is covered in water - by solving the clues below.

The clues provide, in reading order, the length of every run of consecutive shaded squares in each row and column. There must be a gap of at least one empty square between each run of shaded squares in the same row or column.

Column clues:

		1													
	2	5	1	2	3				1	5	3				
	2	6	8	6	6	4	2	2	1	2	2	4			
5	3	2	2	1	1	5	5	1	2	1	2	2	9	5	

Row clues:

- 5
- 3, 2, 2
- 4, 1, 2
- 3, 2, 4
- 5, 1, 4
- 1, 3, 2, 1, 2
- 1, 5, 3
- 1, 5, 4
- 1, 4, 4
- 2, 2, 3
- 1, 4, 1
- 2, 4, 2
- 2, 2, 2
- 2, 2, 3
- 5

A LAYERED EARTH

The ground beneath our feet may seem solid, but in fact most of the inside of Earth is made of metal and rock that is so hot that it stays in liquid form.

There are four main layers that make up Earth's structure. Can you match the names to the correct layers of Earth?

CRUST   INNER CORE   MANTLE   OUTER CORE

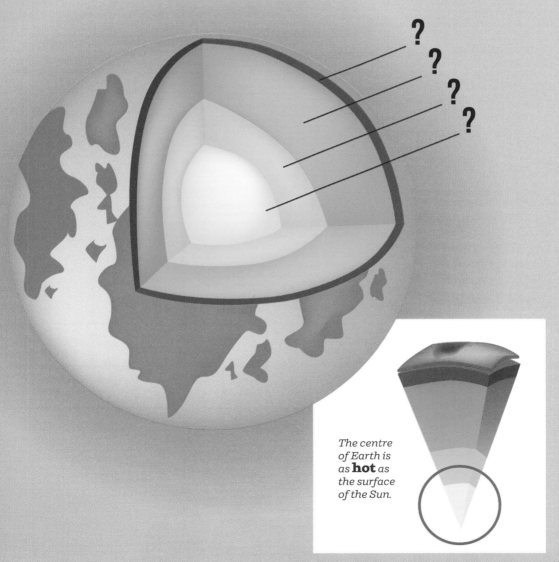

?
?
?
?

*The centre of Earth is as **hot** as the surface of the Sun.*

• • •
PERMISSION TO LAND

DID YOU KNOW?

Sunsets are blue on Mars because of the way light enters the planet's atmosphere.

In the last century, space technology has advanced so much that we can now land spacecraft successfully on Mars - which is 33.9 million miles (54.5 million km) from Earth, at its closest point.

Imagine that you're directing a ship to land on Mars, and you know there are several huge boulders you need to avoid when touching down. Your landing craft has sent back the numeric data below, showing the number of boulders in various areas of the surface. Can you locate the exact location of the individual boulders?

To help you locate the boulders, number clues are given, where each number reveals the exact count of how many boulders are found in its touching squares, including diagonally touching squares. No more than one boulder can be found in a single square, and boulders aren't found in squares which contain numbers.

1					3		1
1			2	2			3
	3				3		
1		2		1			3
	3		2		1		1
1				1		1	
						2	1
	2	2	2			2	

MATHEMATICAL MARS

Test your maths skills with these three questions about Mars.

? Mars is home to the huge volcano Olympus Mons, which is 2.5 times higher than Earth's tallest volcano, Mauna Kea. Mauna Kea's peak is 4,200m (13,780ft) above sea level, and its bottom is 5,800m (19,030ft) below the surface of the ocean. Given these facts, how tall is Olympus Mons?

? Earth and Mars are 33.9 million miles (54.5 million km) apart when at their closest points in their orbits. If a spacecraft heading straight from Earth to Mars travelled 3 million miles (4.82 million km) a month, how long would it take to get there?

? Mars takes 687 days to make a complete orbit round the Sun. How many Mars years have been completed by the time 20 Earth years are complete?

*The highest mountain in the Solar System is on **Mars** (below). It's called Olympus Mons and is a volcano three times the height of Everest, and roughly the size of the state of Arizona.*

THE NIGHT SKY

There is so much to see in the night sky, although much of it is hidden if you view it from a built-up location with lots of light pollution.

Take a close look at these two images of the sky at night. Can you spot ten differences between them?

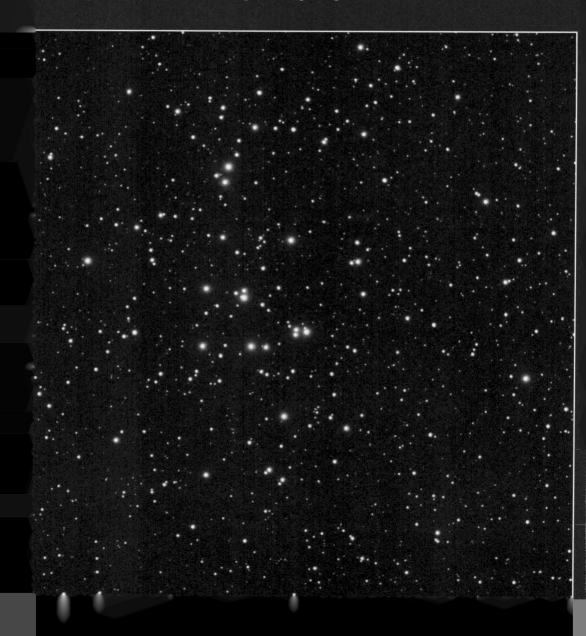

There are **100 billion** stars in just our galaxy – and there are at least 100 billion other galaxies too!

On a clear night, the human eye can see around 19 quadrillion miles (that's 19 followed by 15 zeroes).

19,000,000,000,000,000

ART IN THE SKY

Some stars in the night sky are brighter than others, and if you join them together they might look like a recognisable shape - perhaps an animal or a person. Some stars have been grouped into shapes like this, and are called constellations.

In the puzzle below is a constellation. Join the dots in increasing numerical order to find out what's hiding in the night sky. When you reach a number with a hollow star, lift your pen and start again at the next number, which will have a solid star. The red dots/stars show the actual stars in the sky - the black dots/stars show the outline of the picture they are said to form. Can you see what it's said to represent?

Aries　　　Taurus　　　Gemini　　　Cancer　　　Leo　　　Virgo

IT'S A SIGN

Hidden in the wordsearch below are the twelve signs of the zodiac, all named after constellations. The dates associated with each constellation were originally based on when the Sun was in their sector of the sky throughout the year. But can you find them all in the wordsearch grid below?

```
A N A T N O I L E H T E T N T
T C O H H R R D R I T H E T C
H H C I E E A H S R E S H E E
T T E E P M T I A S S E E C R
G H R B G R H W E A W C T T N
T E A T U L O A I A C H B E E
T S E T W L G C T N E A D E F
E C T R H O L E S C S I H I R
R A H E A E R I R E A S G F A
S L E T G B R A H M H E E D D
E E R W E I B A E S T T H E T
B S E A B S T H M H T A I M T
H S R E T U T E E A T H D H E
R E H C R A E H T H C E O H H
R S E R R L T H S I F E H T R
```

Different cultures created different constellations, but even those in common across cultures often have different stories behind them. For example, to the Yolngu in Australia, the constellation of **Orion** *is made up of three brothers, whereas to the ancient Greeks it was the form of a hunter. That said, the constellation appears upside down in the Southern Hemisphere, relative to the Northern Hemisphere, which could account for the difference.*

THE ARCHER
THE BULL
THE CRAB
THE FISH
THE LION

THE MAIDEN
THE RAM
THE SCALES
THE SCORPION
THE SEA-GOAT

THE TWINS
THE WATER
BEARER

▼
The zodiac constellations
no longer quite align with their given months. The tilt in Earth's axis causes the position of the Sun in the sky at a certain point in the year to slowly change over time.

Libra

Scorpio

Sagittarius

Capricorn

Aquarius

Pisces

HEATING UP

The Sun is so hot that we can feel its heat on Earth, even though it's around 93 million miles (150 million km) away from us. Its surface is a massive 6,000°C, but its centre is an unbelievable 15 million°C!

The temperatures in the puzzle (right) are somewhat cooler, ranging as they do from 1°C to 9°C. Complete the set of temperature measurements by placing a digit from 1 to 9 in each empty square, so that no number repeats in any row, column or bold-lined 3x3 box. Also, digits placed on the thermometers must increase in value from the bulb to the head of each thermometer, so every digit along the length of the thermometer must be greater than all of the digits before it.

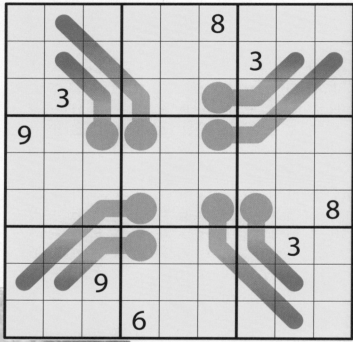

Sometimes the Sun releases a stream of charged particles known as **"solar wind"**. When it reaches Earth it can cause electrical interference, among other effects.

SOLAR SHADOWS

The Sun's energy creates both heat and light – two key factors in making life on Earth possible. But wherever the Sun shines, it also casts a shadow.

Have a look at the shadows below. Can you work out which one belongs to the plant shown?

A

B

C

D

WHAT TIME IS IT?

*Sometimes, particularly in scientific contexts, **GMT** is also known as **UTC**, short for "Universal Time Coordinated".*

Earth continuously spins around on its axis, in addition to orbiting the Sun. It takes 24 hours for Earth to make a complete spin, which is why that's the length of a day. Every 24 hours, the same part of Earth points at the Sun, and while half of the planet is facing the Sun, the rest is facing away. Therefore, countries around the world are split into different time zones, so that daylight and night occur at similar times of day.

Time zones are measured based on their horizontal distance from a vertical line that runs from the North Pole to the South Pole via Greenwich in London. It's called the prime meridian, and all the time zones in the world are based on it. Time at the meridian is known as Greenwich Mean Time, or GMT for short. If your time zone is four hours ahead of London, for example, then we say it is GMT +4, and if it's 4 hours behind then it's GMT -4.

Have a look at the following cities and the time zones they are in, then see if you can answer the questions beneath.

TIME ZONES

LONDON	GMT
SHANGHAI	GMT +8
CHICAGO	GMT -5
SYDNEY	GMT +10
BUENOS AIRES	GMT -3

? If it's 12pm in London, what time is it in Sydney?

? What time is it in London if it's 7.30pm in Buenos Aires?

? At 10am in Chicago, what time is it in Shanghai?

? If it's 5pm in Buenos Aires, what time is it in Sydney?

RISE AND SHINE

The Sun creates light for Earth. See if you can light up the puzzle below by adding your own miniature suns to it, according to the rules:

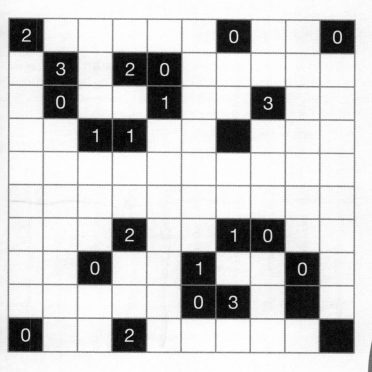

Although **China** *has five geographical time zones, the country officially only uses one, Beijing time.*

- You can add a sun to any empty square, but not a shaded one.
- Light shines out of every sun in both horizontal and vertical directions along the same row and column. Light travels until it reaches either the edge of the grid or a shaded square.
- Some shaded squares have numbers on them. This exact number of suns must be placed in the touching squares (left/right/up/down, but not including diagonally) - no more, and no less.
- Every unshaded square of the grid must be lit by at least one sun.
- No sun can shine on any other sun.

ORBITAL ORIENTATION

The planets in our Solar System orbit in a roughly circular path around the Sun. The planets each have their own orbit, and the further away a planet is from the Sun, the longer it takes for it to travel around it once – which means that the further out from the Sun you get, the longer a year is.

People used to think that the Sun orbited Earth, and that you would **fall off** *the edge of the world if you walked far enough.*

Take a look at the picture below for a minute and try to memorise the positions of the planets – including the dwarf planet Pluto – in their orbits at one particular point in time. When you're ready, cover up the picture and then see if you can draw them back in the same positions on the page opposite. Can you remember which planet was where?

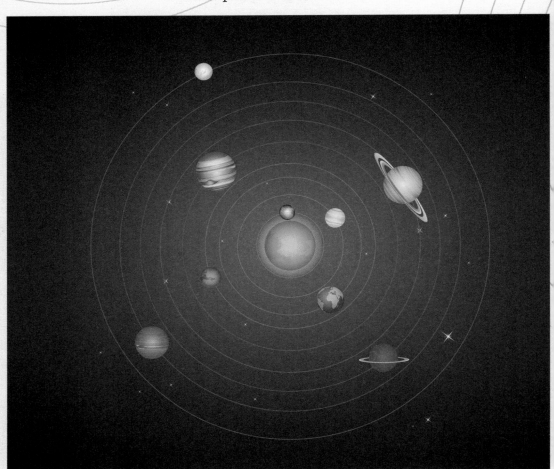

*It takes **Uranus** 84 Earth years to complete one orbit of the Sun – but that's nothing compared to Neptune, which takes a massive 165 Earth years!*

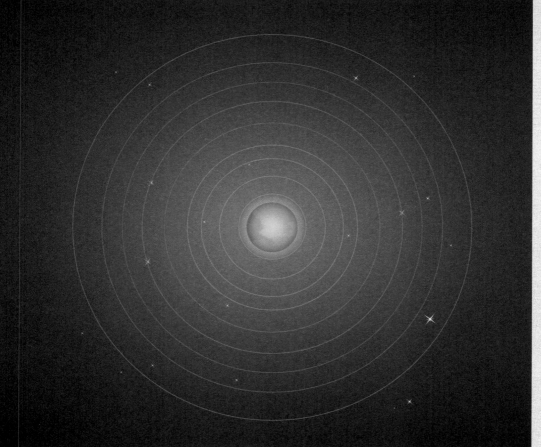

DID YOU KNOW?

All the **tides** on Earth are created by gravity caused by the movement of the Moon around Earth.

Most planets have moons orbiting around the planet, just as the planets in turn orbit the Sun. Earth only has one moon, but some planets have many moons. Jupiter has the most in the Solar System, with around 80.

In the grid below, some of the moons have become separated from their planets. Can you help reunite them by drawing a path between planets and moons of the same colour? The paths cannot cross over, and no more than one path can enter any square.

The **footprints** left by humans on the Moon (below) could remain there for millions of years, since there is no wind or water to wash or blow them away.

The Moon moves approximately **3.8cm (1 ½ in)** further away from Earth every year.

MONOCHROME MOONS

A small spacecraft is flying in a loop around the many moons of Jupiter. Can you plot its exact route by drawing a single loop on the grid below?

The loop must consist of straight lines moving horizontally and vertically between some squares, but without visiting any square more than once. It must pass over every moon (both black and white), but need not visit every other square.

The spacecraft must travel straight through the squares both before and after black moons on its loop, and the spacecraft must make a 90 degree turn as it passes over the moon itself. Conversely, the spacecraft must travel straight over white moons without turning, but it must turn in at least one of the squares immediately before or after the moon.

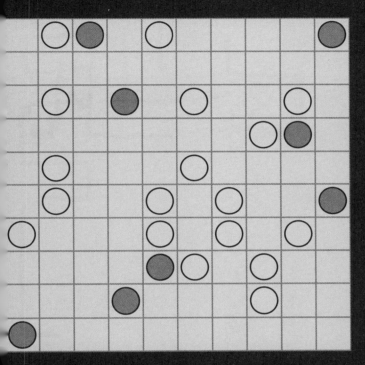

Sometimes the Moon appears larger in the sky, since it's closer to Earth than normal. This is known as a **"supermoon"**.

ASTEROID ASSIGNMENT

The Solar System contains more than just planets, moons and the Sun. If you travel between Mars and Jupiter, for example, you'll find an asteroid belt packed with rocks of many different shapes and sizes, including over 2 million of them that are larger than half a mile in diameter. The bigge[] asteroid, Ceres, is even considered to be a minor planet.

When an asteroid reaches Earth's atmosphere, it's known as a **meteor**. *Most burn up in the sky, but some reach the surface and create huge explosions. The pictured Berringer Crater is one of the best-preserved in the world. It was caused by an impact 50,000 years ago and is around 1,200 metres (3,940ft) in diameter. That is nothing compared to the Vredefort Dome in South Africa which was created around 2 billion years ago, and was over 190 miles (300km) across when it was first formed.*

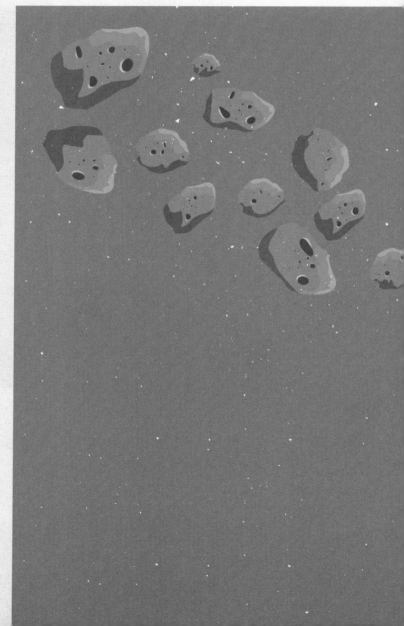

Unlike the asteroids in a real asteroid belt, the asteroids on this page come in identical pairs. Can you draw lines to match each asteroid to its partner elsewhere in the asteroid belt?

Comets *are a bit like asteroids, except they orbit the Sun in extremely elliptical orbits. We currently know of about 3,500 comets in the Solar System, but there are many more that we haven't identified.*

BEAUTY IN THE SKY

The images below are all real photos of the northern lights - also known as the Aurora Borealis - which is a beautiful natural phenomenon that occurs when charged particles from the Sun interact with Earth's atmosphere. It creates amazing light displays, visible in the night sky near Earth's poles - if you're lucky enough to see them.

On the opposite page, colour in the night sky to create your own version of the northern lights. There are no right or wrong answers here - so either make up your own, or base it on one of the images below.

The equivalent of the northern lights in the Southern Hemisphere is known as the **Aurora Australis**, or the southern lights.

DID YOU KNOW?

Interaction with different types of particles in the atmosphere create **different colours** of light – for example, oxygen creates a green or red light, while nitrogen creates orange or red.

HOUSTON, WE HAVE A PUZZLE

DID YOU KNOW?

The word **"astronaut"** means **"star sailor"** in Greek.

Concealed in the puzzle below is something that might be very familiar to space explorers. Colour in the polygons according to the number key in order to reveal a hidden picture.

KEY:

1 = yellow
2 = light orange
3 = orange
4 = red
5 = dark red
6 = dark blue
7 = light grey
8 = grey
9 = white
0 = light blue

The furthest a human has ever been from Earth is when orbiting the Moon. They were around 250,000 miles (400,000km) away – but even that is less than **0.001%** of the distance from Earth to the Sun.

AN ACCIDENTAL ADVENTURE

When an astronaut leaves their spacecraft while in space, it's known as a spacewalk – although it's more like floating than walking! Astronauts are usually tied to their shuttles with a long rope known as a tether in order to make sure they don't drift off into space.

The astronaut in the maze has, however, become separated from his craft! Can you help him find his way back through the maze of tangled tether ropes?

DID YOU KNOW?

The first man in space was **Yuri Gagarin**, in April 1961, while the first woman was **Valentina Tereshkova**, in June 1963.

EXPLORER'S QUIZ

Test your knowledge of this chapter by seeing how well you can remember some of the things we have covered. Congratulations if you can answer the questions without checking back to the previous pages!

DID YOU KNOW?

Before they can go to space, **astronauts** do lots of training in swimming pools to somewhat simulate the lack of gravity in space. One test includes swimming 75 metres (246ft) – while wearing a full flight suit and tennis shoes.

? What galaxy do we live in?

? Who was the first woman in space?

? What is the name of the brightest star in the sky?

? What is the name for the layer of molten rock directly underneath Earth's crust?

? Which is the largest planet in the Solar System?

? What is it called when an astronaut explores outside of their spacecraft?

? What is the name of the largest volcano on Mars?

? What is the Aurora Borealis more commonly known as?

? Roughly how many moons does Jupiter have?

? How many Earth days is a year on Mars?

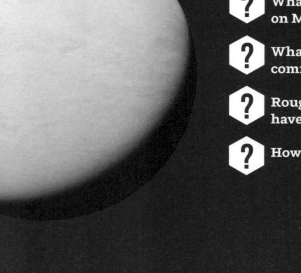

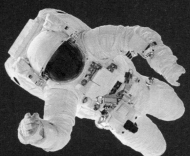

MOON MATCH

On the left below is a list of planets from our Solar System, and on the right you can see the names of some of the moons that orbit them. Can you match the moons to the planets they orbit?

To give you a hint, in this puzzle Jupiter has four moons, Saturn has three, Neptune has two and Earth has one.

PLANETS	MOONS
EARTH	CALLISTO
	DIONE
NEPTUNE	EUROPA
	GANYMEDE
SATURN	IO
	PROTEUS
JUPITER	RHEA
	THE MOON
	TITAN
	TRITON

200

◄ There are almost 200 known **moons** in the Solar System.

CHAPTER 4:
DINOSAURS

DIG FOR DINOSAURS

The term **"dinosaur"** was first used in 1842 by the English palaeontologist Richard Owen. It comes from Greek and means **"terrible lizard"**.

Dinosaurs were a group of reptiles that dominated the planet for over 140 million years. Over that incredibly long amount of time, they evolved into diverse shapes and sizes, from the fearsome giant *Spinosaurus* to the chicken-sized *Microraptor*.

We know all about dinosaurs from the fossils we find in the ground. These had been preserved in the earth for hundreds of millions of years until palaeontologists - scientists who study dinosaurs - first began to realise what they were in the early 1800s. Now scientists are at work all around the world uncovering more and more fossils, increasing our understanding of these magnificent animals that once ruled the world!

Dippy the Diplodocus *lived in the Natural History Museum in London from 1905 until 2017, when he started a tour around the UK. Despite how real he looks, he was not a real fossil, but a cast of a fossil carefully made from the fragile original bones. The fossil from which Dippy is moulded lived around 150 million years ago in what is now Wyoming, USA. He is 21.3 metres long, which isn't even as big as Diplodocus can grow - the biggest could reach a massive 26 metres in length! Despite that, you would probably have been safe to be near this friendly giant. They were herbivores, meaning they only eat vegetation, and they used their long neck to reach the highest leaves, much like giraffes do today.*

Microraptor was small (42–120cm, 16–47in), four-winged and sported flight feathers on its legs.

Help dig for these dinosaurs in this wordsearch!

```
X V S C H S U R U A S O G E T S
E O E E E L A U S P U T I S B H
R T U L L S R A O U R O N U R I
S O B P O U A O S I R C O A O I
U L I R S C U S C O S U T T N O
R S N S A U I E A U V U O S T L
U G S A N C R R R I R B U P O B
A A D L S A H U A C L C S I S C
S T S A T I A I A P O S O N A O
O N O O P S U G O D T S N O U A
N E P T O R R A O S T O H S R A
N S U L P R E L A O A R R A U X
A I L R P U P A R R R U U U S R
R A T U N I S S O O S E R R C S
Y S N O D O N A U G I U U U L O
T U R U P U L O O U V S P S S S
```

ALLOSAURUS
BRACHIOSAURUS
BRONTOSAURUS
DIPLODOCUS
IGUANODON
SPINOSAURUS
STEGOSAURUS
TRICERATOPS
TYRANNOSAURUS REX
VELOCIRAPTOR

Spinosaurus was huge (15–16m, 49–52ft long) with 1.8 metre (6ft) spines on its back, forming a large fin.

DINOSAUR DIVISION

TINYSAURS

The dinosaurs in the **Triassic Period** were small. They only began to grow larger and more dominant after a mass extinction wiped out many other animal species at the beginning of the Jurassic Period.

Dinosaurs lived on Earth many millions of years ago. The last dinosaurs died out 66 million years ago, but there had been dinosaurs on Earth for almost 190 million years before that, during a time period known as the Mesozoic Era. Scientists who study this era split it up into three different sections, known as the Triassic, Jurassic and Cretaceous Periods.

Below are these three time periods, and a list of dinosaurs that were alive during the Mesozoic Era. Can you sort them into the time periods they were alive during, using lines to match them up?

TIME PERIODS

TRIASSIC
[251–199 million years ago]

JURASSIC
[199–145 million years ago]

CRETACEOUS
[145–66 million years ago]

DINOSAURS

ALLOSAURUS

ANKYLOSAURUS

ARCHAEOPTERYX

DIPLODOCUS

MUSSAURUS

PLATEOSAURUS

RIOJASAURUS

STAURIKOSAURUS

STEGOSAURUS

TRICERATOPS

TYRANNOSAURUS REX

VELOCIRAPTOR

EASY AS TJC

Can you place each of the three periods in the Mesozoic Era - the **Triassic**, **Jurassic** and **Cretaceous** - into the grid below, so that each appears exactly once in every row and column? Use the letter T for Triassic, J for Jurassic and C for Cretaceous. The letters around the outside of the grid show you which of the three time periods is encountered first in that row or column, reading inwards from the outside. Two squares in each row and column will remain empty.

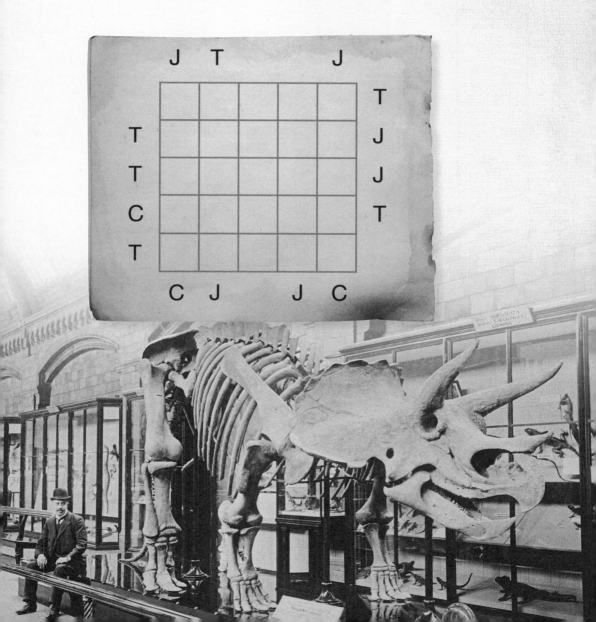

PANGEA PUZZLE

Have a look at the map of the world opposite. This is what Earth used to look like! Millions of years ago, the areas that we now know as separate continents were all joined together in one supercontinent, known as Pangea (or Pangaea).

Although the continents have slowly changed their position on the globe over millions of years, they haven't changed shape that much. Can you label the map of Pangea with the names of the land masses it will split up into?

Think carefully about what a map of the world looks like today and use the outlines to help you.

DID YOU KNOW?

The word **Pangea** comes from the Greek *pan* meaning "whole" and *gaia* meaning "Earth".

The Atlas Mountains *in Morocco, and the Appalachian Mountains in the USA, used to be part of the same mountain chain: the Central Pangean Mountains.*

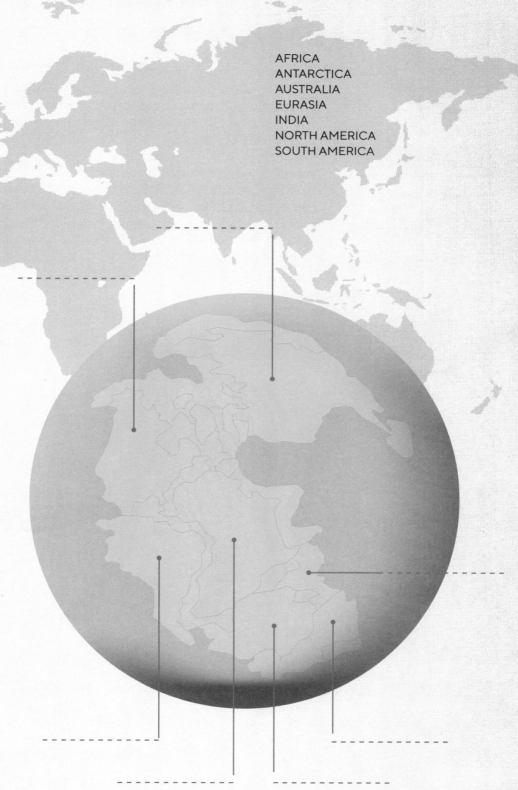

AFRICA
ANTARCTICA
AUSTRALIA
EURASIA
INDIA
NORTH AMERICA
SOUTH AMERICA

FUN WITH FOSSILS

DINOSAURS

DID YOU KNOW?

The largest **T. rex** fossil was discovered in Canada. Named "Scotty" it would have weighed over 8,800kg (8.6 tons) and is estimated to have been around 30 years old.

Sometimes palaeontologists are lucky enough to discover whole dinosaur skeletons underground, which can be pieced together to learn more about how the animal lived.

Have a look at the skeleton below from a *Stegosaurus* that lived about 150 million years ago. You'll notice that some of the bones are missing and have to be added to the skeleton before it's complete. Can you match the loose bones provided to the spaces in order to complete the skeleton?

Many of the dinosaurs from the 1993 film **Jurassic Park** *were alive in the later Cretaceous Period, such as the* T. rex *and* Velociraptors.

KEEP OUT!

When a new dinosaur fossil is discovered, it's important to fence it off to protect it from damage until it can be dug up. In the puzzle below is a newly unearthed dinosaur. Can you complete the fence around the site by joining all of these fence posts?

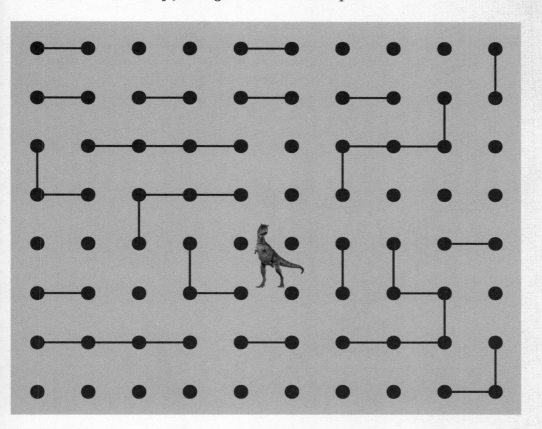

The fence should form a loop that visits every post exactly once, without crossing over or touching itself at any point. Only horizontal and vertical lines can be drawn between fence posts (dots), since the fence is constructed from fixed-size panels.

Animals such as insects, lizards and scorpions have been found fossilized in **amber**, which is itself made of fossilized tree sap. One piece of amber has even been found with fossilized dinosaur feathers inside.

PAIRS OF PRINTS

In Lark Quarry in Australia, there's footprint evidence of a **dinosaur stampede**, involving 150 small dinosaurs being ambushed by much larger predators.

As well as finding bones and fossils, evidence of dinosaur footprints can occasionally be found preserved in rock. They were left behind by dinosaurs who stood in mud or soft clay, and the deep prints they made were later preserved as rocks with an almost exact cast of their footprints.

Have a look at the footprints left on the rocks below. Can you match up these pairs of dinosaur footprints?

1 METRE

The biggest dinosaur footprint ever found belongs to a **Brachiosaur**. It measures nearly 1 metre (3 $\frac{1}{3}$ ft) across!

DINOSAUR DECISIONS

Can you sort these dinosaurs into order of average length, from smallest to largest? If you're not sure, guess!

- **Brachiosaurus**
- **Microraptor**
- **Spinosaurus**
- **Stegosaurus**
- **Tyrannosaurus rex**

The neck of a *Diplodocus* could grow to be over 6 metres (20ft) long – that's taller than a giraffe!

? If a giraffe's neck was 1.5 metres (5ft) long, roughly how many times taller could a fully grown *Diplodocus's* neck be?

One of the largest known dinosaurs was the *Argentinosaurus*, which lived in the late Cretaceous Period. It probably weighed around 100,000kg (98 tons), making it one of the largest land-living animals of all time. By contrast, a male African elephant weighs around 5,000kg (4.9 tons).

? How many African elephants would you need to make a group that weighed as much as two *Argentinosaurus*?

•••

SIZE ASSIGNMENT

Different sizes of dinosaur coexisted, but kept to themselves. Can you arrange the dinosaurs in the following grid so that one of each size is placed in each row and column?

To show how they fit, arrows between some pairs of squares point at the square which contains the smaller of the two dinosaurs in that pair of squares.

*It's hard to imagine a world without **flowers** in it, but before the Mesozoic Era there were no flowering plants on Earth.*

5

4

3

2

1

DINOSAURS

DINO IN DISGUISE

DINOSAURS

Colour in the sections in the picture below according to the number key to reveal a hidden dinosaur from the Cretaceous Period.

KEY:

1 = brown
2 = dark brown
3 = purple
4 = dark purple
5 = yellow
6 = light orange
7 = green
8 = dark green
9 = light blue
0 = light grey

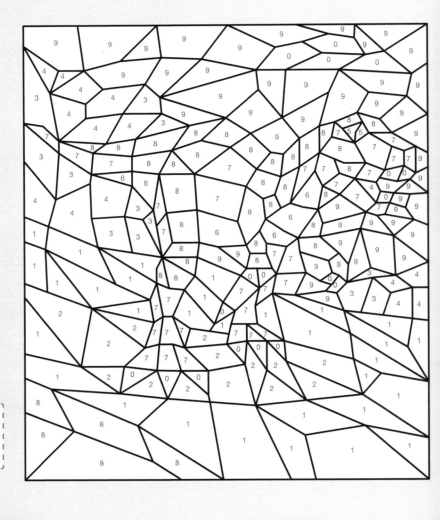

In 1824, the **Megalosaurus** *became the first dinosaur to be given a name. It means "great lizard".*

HIDDEN GIANT

Concealed in this puzzle is one of the longest dinosaurs. Can you reveal it by shading in the correct squares?

The clues provide, in reading order, the length of every run of consecutive shaded squares in each row and column. There must be a gap of at least one empty square between each run of shaded squares in the same row or column.

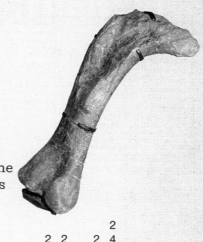

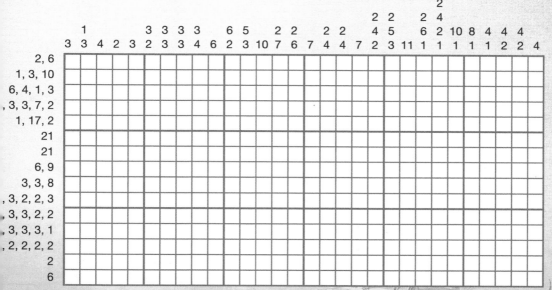

Row clues (top to bottom):
- 2, 6
- 1, 3, 10
- 6, 4, 1, 3
- , 3, 3, 7, 2
- 1, 17, 2
- 21
- 21
- 6, 9
- 3, 3, 8
- , 3, 2, 2, 3
- , 3, 3, 2, 2
- , 3, 3, 3, 1
- , 2, 2, 2, 2
- 2
- 6

Column clues (reading order):
2
2 2 — 2 4
1 — 3 3 3 3 — 6 5 — 2 2 — 2 2 — 4 5 — 6 2 10 8 4 4 4
3 3 4 2 3 2 3 3 4 6 2 3 10 7 6 7 4 4 7 2 3 11 1 1 1 1 1 1 2 2 4

Dinosaurs can be split into two groups based on their body type. They can be either "lizard hipped" or "bird hipped". Both dinosaurs in these two puzzles belong to the "lizard hipped" group, known as **Saurischia**.

A MULTICOLOUR MYSTERY

*Some species of fish which are still alive today, such as the **hagfish, coelacanth** and **sawfish**, first appeared during the Mesozoic Era.*

Although we know a lot about the shapes and sizes of dinosaurs from bones and fossils, we don't really know what colour dinosaurs were on the outside. They might have been dull grey or brown to help with camouflage, or perhaps they were a mixture of bright and contrasting colours, like modern birds of paradise.

The picture below has been left blank for you to imagine what colour the dinosaurs were. Be as creative as you like!

The Diplodocus *skeleton known as* **"Dippy"** *is one of the most famous dinosaur skeletons in the world. It was first discovered in 1899 and many casts were made which have travelled all over the world. Dippy was the first dinosaur millions of people had ever seen, and is largely responsible for the popularity of dinosaurs with the general public.*

AN EGGS-TRAORDINARY FIND

Dinosaur eggs
*were much more
spherical than most
bird eggs.*

All dinosaurs - like most reptiles - laid eggs to reproduce, and palaeontologists have found fossilized evidence of dinosaur nests. It's possible that baby dinosaurs of some species might have walked away from their nests straight after hatching, while other hatchlings might have stayed in their nests to be fed by their parents, just as birds are.

Take a look at the two dinosaur nests on these pages. Can you spot ten differences between them?

Dinosaurs may have laid many eggs at once in order to give the group of young dinosaurs a better **chance of survival**.

HERDS AND HUNTING

When groups of fossilized footprints are found together, they are known as **"trackways"**.

Large groups of dinosaur footprints are often found together, suggesting that some dinosaurs may have lived in herds. There are good reasons to live in herds, since moving in large groups can offer protection from predators, which can be especially important when there are young dinosaurs in the herd.

The dinosaur in the maze to the right has been separated from the rest of the herd. Can you guide it through the maze of tall winding paths to get it back to its parents?

VICIOUS VELOCIRAPTORS

Velociraptors were predatory carnivores, hunting other dinosaurs and attacking them with sharp claws. If they were alive today, you certainly wouldn't want to come across one!

2	4			3		2	1
		5		5			
3		3		3			2
	2					3	
	3			1			2
3		3		1		3	
		3			4		2
	2						1

The name
"Velociraptor"
means
"swift thief".

Hidden in the grid above are some *Velociraptors* you want to avoid. Number clues have been given to help you work out where they're lurking, where each number reveals the exact count of how many *Velociraptors* are found in its touching squares, including diagonally touching squares. No more than one *Velociraptor* can be found in a single square, and *Velociraptors* aren't found in squares which contain numbers.

DINO DOT-TO-DOTS

DINOSAURS

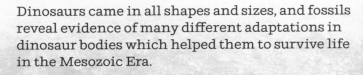

Some armoured dinosaurs, such as the **Ankylosaurus**, *were herbivores and had armour to defend themselves from predators.*

Dinosaurs came in all shapes and sizes, and fossils reveal evidence of many different adaptations in dinosaur bodies which helped them to survive life in the Mesozoic Era.

Hidden on these pages are two dinosaurs that you might recognise from their distinctive outlines. Join the dots in increasing numerical order to reveal their shapes - and see what they might have used to defend themselves. When you reach a number with a hollow star, lift your pen and start again at the next number, which will have a solid star.

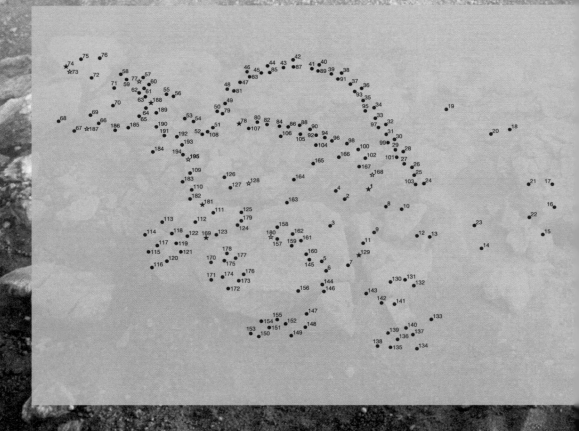

The **Stegosaurus** had huge spiny plates on its body, but these were most likely used to help keep it cool rather than as armour.

TREASURE TROVE

The **tongue-twister**
"She Sells Seashells on the Seashore" is said to have been inspired by Mary Anning.

The first complete **ichthyosaur** skull was found by Mary Anning's brother, Joseph.

Not all animals alive during the Mesozoic Era were dinosaurs – many other animals lived on Earth alongside them. Although we don't know of any dinosaurs that lived underwater, a group of marine reptiles did live in the ocean at the same time and shared many similar characteristics with the dinosaurs.

The most well-known of these extinct marine reptiles were ichthyosaurs and plesiosaurs, and some of the most complete skeletons were found by a woman called Mary Anning in the early 1800s. She found them in Devon, in an area now appropriately known as the Jurassic Coast.

Imagine you're a fossil hunter carefully laying out your finds after a long day's digging. Can you place just two fossils into every row, column, and fenced-off region of this puzzle? Fossils can't be in touching squares, including diagonally touching squares. You can indicate the fossils by shading squares – or trying to draw your own!

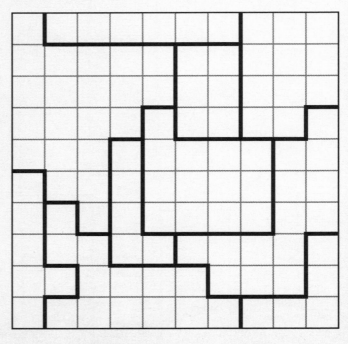

A PTERRIFIC PUZZLE

Hidden in the grid below is an animal you may recognise – but it's not what you think it is! It's often mistaken for a dinosaur, but palaeontologists have shown that it actually belongs to a different scientific family.

Colour in the squares using the number key below to reveal the truth.

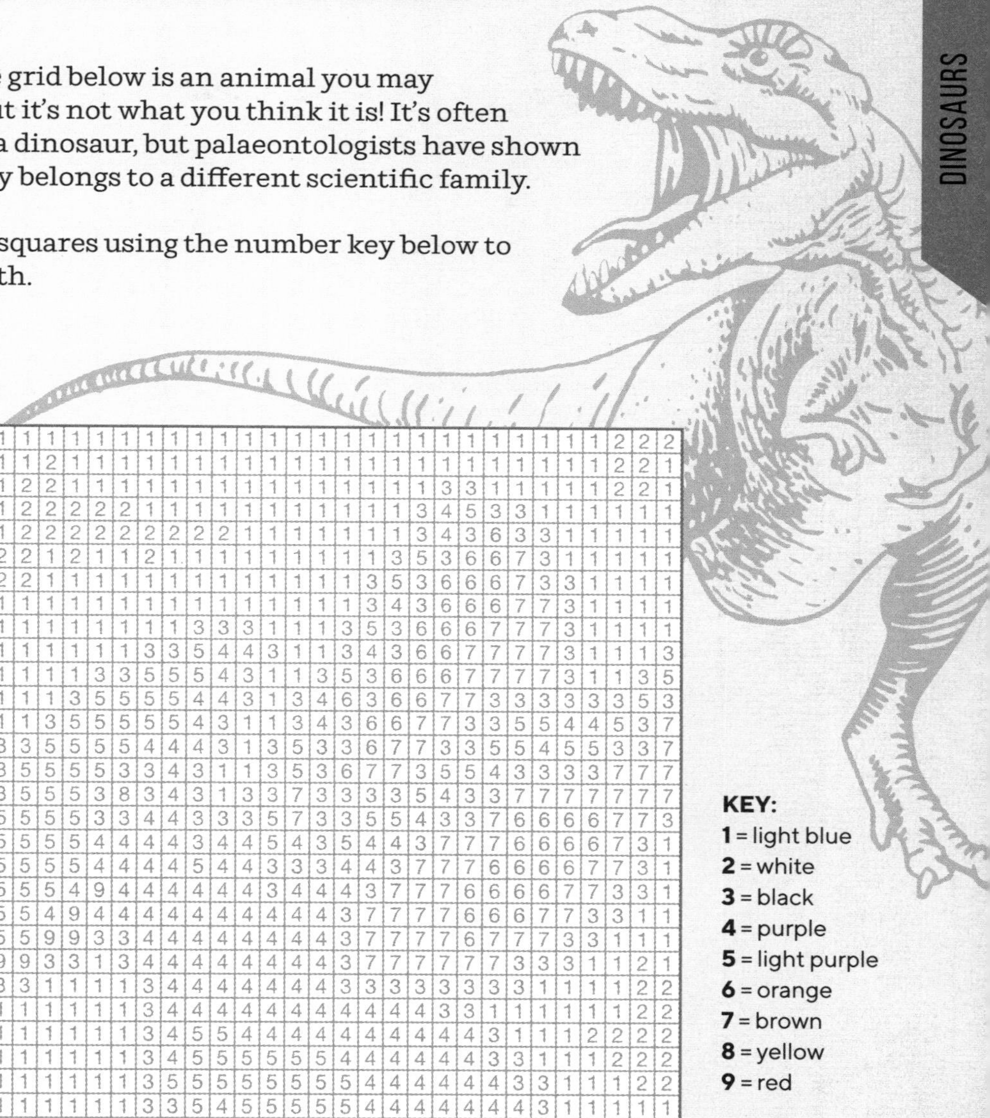

1	1	1	1	1	1	1	1	1	1	1	1	1	1	1	1	1	1	1	1	1	1	1	1	1	1	1	1	1	1	1	1	2	2	2
1	1	1	1	1	1	1	1	1	2	1	1	1	1	1	1	1	1	1	1	1	1	1	1	1	1	1	1	1	1	1	1	2	2	1
1	1	1	1	1	1	1	1	2	2	1	1	1	1	1	1	1	1	1	1	1	1	1	1	1	3	3	1	1	1	1	1	2	2	1
1	1	1	1	1	1	1	1	2	2	2	2	2	1	1	1	1	1	1	1	1	1	1	1	3	4	5	3	3	1	1	1	1	1	1
1	1	1	2	2	2	2	1	2	2	2	2	2	2	2	2	2	1	1	1	1	1	1	1	3	4	3	6	3	3	1	1	1	1	1
1	1	1	2	2	2	2	2	2	1	2	1	1	2	1	1	1	1	1	1	1	1	1	3	5	3	6	6	7	3	1	1	1	1	1
1	1	1	2	2	2	2	2	2	1	1	1	1	1	1	1	1	1	1	1	1	1	3	5	3	6	6	6	7	3	3	1	1	1	1
1	1	1	2	1	1	2	1	1	1	1	1	1	1	1	1	1	1	1	1	1	1	3	4	3	6	6	6	7	7	3	1	1	1	1
1	1	1	1	1	1	1	1	1	1	1	1	1	1	1	3	3	3	1	1	1	3	5	3	6	6	6	7	7	7	3	1	1	1	1
1	1	1	1	1	1	1	1	1	1	1	1	1	3	3	5	4	4	3	1	1	3	4	3	6	6	7	7	7	7	3	1	1	1	3
1	1	1	1	1	1	1	1	1	1	1	3	3	5	5	5	4	3	1	1	3	5	3	6	6	6	7	7	7	7	3	1	1	3	5
1	1	1	1	1	1	1	1	1	1	3	5	5	5	5	4	4	3	1	3	4	6	3	6	6	7	7	3	3	3	3	3	3	5	3
1	1	1	1	1	1	1	1	1	3	5	5	5	5	5	4	3	1	1	3	4	3	6	6	7	7	3	3	5	5	4	4	5	3	7
1	1	1	1	1	1	1	3	3	5	5	5	5	4	4	4	3	1	3	5	3	3	6	7	7	3	3	5	5	4	5	5	3	3	7
1	1	1	1	1	1	3	3	5	5	5	5	3	3	4	3	1	1	3	5	3	6	7	7	3	5	5	4	3	3	3	3	7	7	7
1	1	1	1	1	3	8	3	5	5	5	3	8	3	4	3	1	3	3	7	3	3	3	3	5	4	3	3	7	7	7	7	7	7	7
1	1	1	1	1	3	3	5	5	5	5	3	3	4	4	3	3	3	5	7	3	3	5	5	4	3	3	7	6	6	6	6	7	7	3
1	1	1	1	3	5	5	5	5	5	5	4	4	4	4	3	4	4	5	4	3	5	4	4	3	7	7	7	6	6	6	6	7	3	1
1	1	1	3	5	5	5	5	5	5	5	4	4	4	4	5	4	4	3	3	3	4	4	3	7	7	7	6	6	6	6	7	7	3	1
1	1	1	3	5	5	5	5	5	5	4	9	4	4	4	4	4	4	3	4	4	4	3	7	7	7	6	6	6	6	7	7	3	3	1
1	1	3	5	5	5	5	5	5	4	9	4	4	4	4	4	4	4	4	4	4	3	7	7	7	7	6	6	6	7	7	3	3	1	1
1	3	5	5	5	5	5	5	5	9	9	3	3	4	4	4	4	4	4	4	4	3	7	7	7	7	6	7	7	7	3	3	1	1	1
1	3	5	5	5	5	5	9	9	3	3	1	3	4	4	4	4	4	4	4	4	3	7	7	7	7	7	7	3	3	3	1	1	2	1
1	3	5	5	5	9	9	3	3	1	1	1	1	3	4	4	4	4	4	4	4	3	3	3	3	3	3	3	3	1	1	1	1	2	2
3	5	5	9	9	3	3	1	1	1	1	1	1	3	4	4	4	4	4	4	4	4	4	4	4	3	3	1	1	1	1	1	1	2	2
3	5	9	3	3	1	1	1	1	1	1	1	1	3	4	5	5	4	4	4	4	4	4	4	4	4	4	3	1	1	1	2	2	2	2
1	3	3	1	1	1	1	1	1	1	1	1	1	3	4	5	5	5	5	5	5	4	4	4	4	4	4	3	3	1	1	1	2	2	2
1	1	1	1	1	1	1	1	1	1	1	1	1	3	5	5	5	5	5	5	5	5	4	4	4	4	4	4	3	3	1	1	1	2	2
1	1	1	1	1	1	1	1	1	1	1	1	1	3	3	5	4	5	5	5	5	5	4	4	4	4	4	4	4	3	1	1	1	1	1
1	1	1	1	1	1	1	1	1	1	1	1	1	1	3	5	5	5	5	5	5	5	4	4	4	4	4	4	4	3	1	1	1	1	1
1	1	1	1	1	1	1	1	1	1	1	1	1	1	1	3	5	5	4	4	4	4	4	4	4	4	4	4	4	3	1	1	1	1	1
1	1	1	1	1	1	1	1	1	1	1	1	1	1	1	3	5	5	5	5	4	4	4	4	4	4	4	4	4	3	3	1	1	1	1
1	1	1	1	2	1	1	1	1	1	1	1	1	1	1	3	3	5	5	5	5	4	4	4	4	4	4	4	4	4	3	1	1	1	1
1	1	1	2	2	1	2	2	1	2	1	2	2	1	1	1	3	5	5	5	5	3	4	4	4	5	5	4	4	4	3	1	1	1	1
1	1	1	2	2	2	2	2	2	2	2	2	2	1	1	1	1	3	3	5	5	3	4	4	4	4	5	5	4	4	3	3	1	1	1
1	1	2	2	2	2	1	2	2	1	2	2	2	1	1	1	1	1	3	3	3	3	3	4	4	3	3	3	5	4	4	4	3	1	1
1	2	2	2	1	1	1	2	2	1	1	1	1	1	1	1	1	1	1	1	3	3	3	4	4	3	1	3	3	4	4	4	4	3	1
1	2	1	1	1	1	1	1	1	1	1	1	1	1	1	1	1	1	1	1	1	1	3	4	4	3	3	1	1	3	3	4	4	3	3
2	2	1	1	1	1	1	1	1	1	1	1	1	1	1	1	1	1	1	1	1	1	3	4	4	5	3	1	1	1	3	3	4	5	3
1	1	1	1	1	1	1	1	1	1	1	1	1	1	1	1	1	1	1	1	1	1	1	3	4	5	3	3	1	1	1	3	5	5	3
1	1	1	1	1	1	1	1	1	1	1	1	1	1	1	1	1	1	1	1	1	1	1	1	3	5	5	3	1	1	1	1	3	5	3
1	1	1	1	1	1	1	1	1	1	1	1	1	1	1	1	1	1	1	1	1	1	1	1	1	3	5	3	1	1	1	1	1	3	3
1	1	1	1	1	1	1	1	1	1	1	1	1	1	1	1	1	1	1	1	1	1	1	1	1	1	3	3	1	1	1	1	1	1	1

KEY:

1 = light blue
2 = white
3 = black
4 = purple
5 = light purple
6 = orange
7 = brown
8 = yellow
9 = red

EXTINCTION EVENT

DINOSAURS

DID YOU KNOW?

A huge crater in Mexico known as the **"Chicxulub crater"** was made 66 million years ago, possibly by an asteroid that caused the dinosaurs to die out.

Why are there no dinosaurs alive today? We're not completely certain, but it is likely that a natural catastrophe wiped them out. One theory is that this was an asteroid hitting Earth - debris from the collision would have blocked out the sun's light and stopped plants from growing, meaning dinosaurs would have starved. Another theory involves a catastrophic volcanic eruption.

Take a look at the picture below, and study it carefully. Try and memorise where each dinosaur is standing in this scene and then, when you're done, cover it up. On the page opposite, see if you can draw lines from each dinosaur to its original position in the picture. Then uncover the first page and check your answers.

Not everything died out in the mass extinction event - **mammals** survived. They were all very small during the Cretaceous Period, so they were able to survive, and eventually evolved into many of the animals we know today.

MISSING LINK MATCH

The **Archaeopteryx** had sharp teeth – unlike modern birds.

Although all the dinosaurs died out in a mass extinction event at the end of the Cretaceous Period, some dinosaur-like flying creatures did survive, and evolved into what we recognise today as birds. So if you see a bird outside today, remember that it's a distant relative of dinosaurs!

The picture below shows an *Archaeopteryx*, a flying bird from the Jurassic Period. *Archaeopteryx* fossils were found with feathers and wings, providing a link between dinosaurs and modern birds.

Look closely at the picture, and then at the five shadows around it. Can you tell which shadow belongs to the *Archaeopteryx*?

AN AWESOME ANCESTOR

Did you know that the chicken is thought to be the closest living relative of the *T. rex*?!

Have a look at the grid below. Can you draw a path joining each chicken with its *T. rex* ancestor of the same colour? Each square must have no more than one path passing through it. The paths cannot cross over, and no more than one path can enter any square.

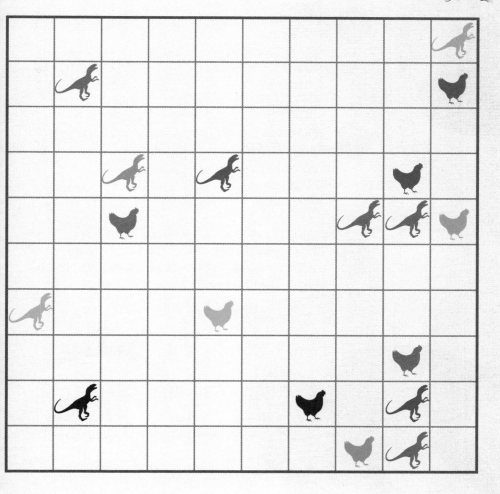

DINO QUIZ

Welcome back to modern times! Were you paying attention while you explored the prehistoric world? See if you can answer the quiz below, using your knowledge gained from this chapter.

 How many time periods were there in the Mesozoic Era?
a) Four
b) Seven
c) Three

 What name is given to a scientist who studies dinosaurs?
a) Palaeontologist
b) Dinaecologist
c) Archaeologist

 What was the single "supercontinent" on Earth known as?
a) Gondwana
b) Pangea
c) Laurasia

 The largest T. rex ever found has been nicknamed "Scotty" – but how big was it?
a) 6,300kg (6.2 tons)
b) 7,500kg (7.4 tons)
c) 8,800kg (8.6 tons)

? **Which dinosaur had the largest feet?**
a) *Diplodocus*
b) *Brachiosaur*
c) *Triceratops*

? **In what country is Lark Quarry, the possible site of a dinosaur stampede?**
a) Australia
b) USA
c) China

? **What is the name of the Devon coast where many prehistoric fossils have been found?**
a) Mesozoic Coast
b) Anning Coast
c) Jurassic Coast

? **Which of these animals was a dinosaur?**
a) *Velociraptor*
b) *Plesiosaur*
c) *Ichthyosaur*

CHAPTER 5:
HUMAN EVOLUTION

WHAT IS EVOLUTION?

The living things all around us haven't always looked and lived the way they do now. Instead, they have evolved over many years to adapt to their environments, changing their appearance and behaviour in order to increase their chance of survival. With each new generation, changes may be introduced. If those changes help the animal or plant to survive, they are more likely to be passed on to subsequent generations than those changes that don't help.

The word **"theory"** in science doesn't necessarily mean something isn't a fact. So even though we call it the "theory" of evolution, it doesn't mean that we aren't certain if it is true or not. Evolution is so well-established that no serious scientist doubts that it is true.

The theory of human evolution explains how modern human beings, known as *Homo sapiens*, descended from great apes, a group whose living members also includes gorillas, orangutans and chimpanzees. The apes began to walk on two feet, leaving their arms free for other tasks, which then allowed for use of tools. Eventually, they began to communicate in more sophisticated ways, which ultimately led to language – and the modern world.

Science Sussed

Once humans had evolved speech, they were able to develop knowledge by communicating with one another. Over time, the sum of human knowledge grew more advanced. Gradually, humans could build on the knowledge of their ancestors in order to discover more about the world.

Can you match the scientists below to their most famous work or discovery - and then find their name in the wordsearch?

```
G I E L I L A G O E L I L A G C
N N G N I R U T N A L A L I G K
N I I D A I W R K E I M E N U C
R R A M R G I N W I A R I M H I
N L E I E L C A G R S K E A U R
O R C N K L C E Y H W H R R T C
T W L A N D F A D A N L E I D D
W L A A E E N R H N E L C E R N
E A S E H N J N E S R I D C I A
N N T A I K E D D D W E N U R N
C F W N P H I A R H N P I R L O
A A G L P S R A C A A A E I A S
A L L E C W D O N A W I X E E T
S C T L I N I E A W N D N E M A
I S N N S T N D N L E S E E L W
W A L B E R T E I N S T E I N A
```

CHARLES DARWIN	*Discovered the structure of DNA*
WATSON AND CRICK	*Developed the smallpox vaccine*
MARY ANNING	*Proposed the theory of evolution*
MARIE CURIE	*Discovered the four main moons of Jupiter*
ALEXANDER FLEMING	*Developed the theory of relativity*
ISAAC NEWTON	*Discovered the antibiotic penicillin*
ALAN TURING	*Predicted the existence of black holes*
EDWARD JENNER	*Developed core theories in computer science*
GALILEO GALILEI	*Discovered radioactivity*
STEPHEN HAWKING	*Made important fossil discoveries*
ALBERT EINSTEIN	*Discovered the laws of motion and gravity*

DOT-TO-DOT DISCOVERY

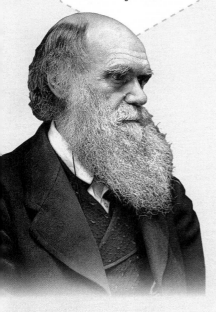

Charles Darwin's most famous journey was aboard the **HMS Beagle**, where he began to put together his scientific theories.

The theory of evolution was developed by Charles Darwin, who travelled the world investigating many different animal species.

Hidden in the puzzle below is an animal that helped him to create his theory, after he noticed that difference species belonging to the same group had remarkably different body shapes. He determined that they had all adapted the shapes of their bodies in order to take advantage of the different types of food available on the island where they were found, and he concluded that other animals did the same to survive too.

Join the dots in increasing numerical order to reveal Darwin's helper. When you reach a hollow star, lift your pencil off the page and start again from the next number, which will be a solid star.

THE MISSING LINK

Darwin's theory of evolution began the journey of explaining how human beings evolved from apes, our closest living relatives. We split from what would evolve into chimpanzees about 8 million years ago, and there are many missing links along the journey from then to now.

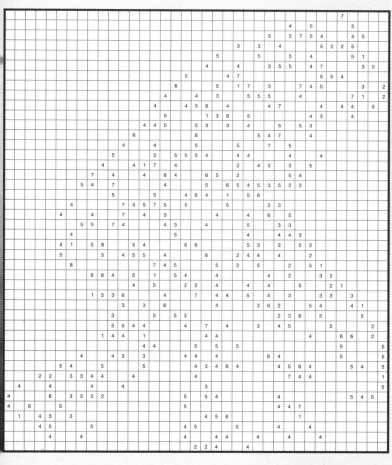

Our closest genetic relatives are chimpanzees and **bonobos**. *We share almost 99% of our DNA with them!*

In the puzzle above, all of the links are missing. Can you draw them in to reveal one of our ancestral missing links? Each number must be joined to another number of the same value. A path of length 1 means simply shade the square with the "1" in it; a path of length 2 must connect to a "2" in a square immediately beside it, creating a 2-square link; while a 3 must link to a "3" in a square two squares away, creating a 3-square link, and so on. No links can cross each other, or move diagonally. Shade all of the linked squares. What do you see?

ODD SKULL OUT

Have a look at the skulls below. They all come from Neanderthals, an early species of human who lived about 40,000 years ago. They're all identical - except one. Can you tell which one it is?

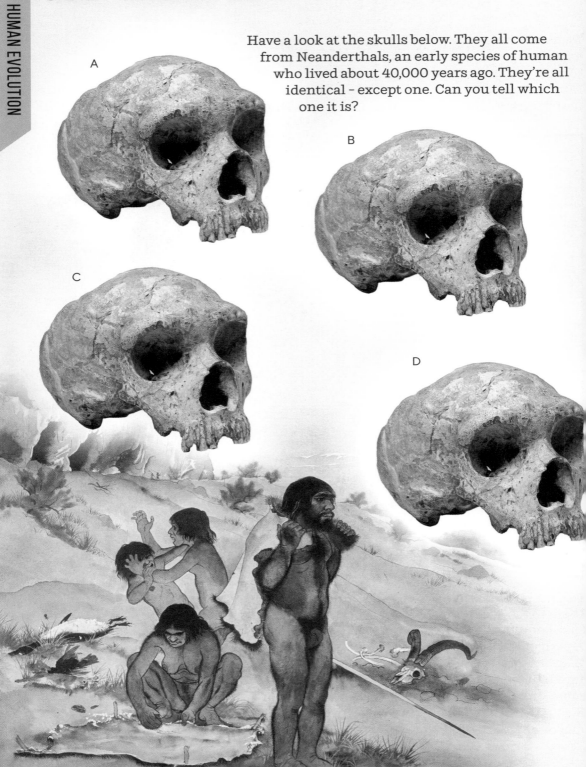

A

B

C

D

LAND BRIDGES

Scientists believe that modern human beings first evolved in Africa, and then slowly migrated around the world. Eventually they settled on every continent.

The gap between what is now Russia and Alaska used to be joined together with a land bridge, meaning that early humans could have crossed over into North America before the continents split apart. There's now a stretch of sea between them called the Bering Strait.

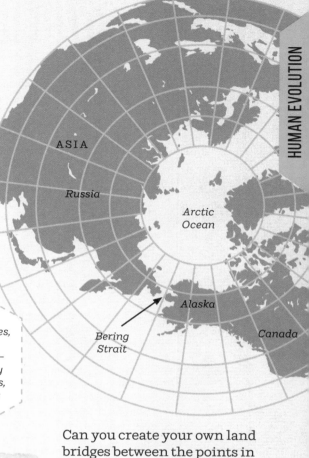

In winter, when the **Bering Strait** *freezes, it's possible to walk from Russia to Alaska – although it's extremely difficult and dangerous, due to the continuous movement of the ice.*

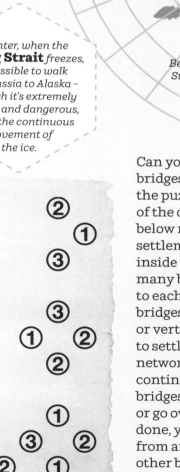

Can you create your own land bridges between the points in the puzzle to the left? Each of the circles in the puzzle below represents a new settlement, and the numbers inside tell you exactly how many bridges must connect to each settlement. Draw bridges either horizontally or vertically from settlement to settlement to make a network across the imaginary continents, making sure that bridges don't cross one another or go over settlements. Once done, you must be able to travel from any settlement to any other by using bridges. No more than one bridge can join any pair of settlements.

147

SABRE-TOOTHED SWEEP

Sabre-toothed cats died out about 12,000 years ago, but this means that they co-existed for a while with early modern humans. Although we've not found any evidence that either species hunted the other, you certainly wouldn't have wanted to get into a fight with one, given their vicious fangs!

Imagine you're living in a forest, and you know there are some sabre-toothed cats lurking in the trees that you don't want to disturb. The numbers in the grid below tell you how many cats there are in the squares surrounding each numbered square, including diagonally. Mark where you think the cats are hiding but remember: there aren't any hiding in the squares with numbers already in them. No more than one cat can be found in any single square.

The best-known sabre-toothed cat was the **Smilodon** – also known as the sabre-toothed tiger. Smilodon teeth grew up to 28cm (11in) long. Ouch!

	3		3			1	
	4			2	3		
	4	3			2		
1	2		2	1		2	2
		1			2	2	
		1	2			3	
	2			4		3	

MEMORY MUDDLE

Have a look at the six cavemen below and try to and memorise their poses. Then, when you think you can remember them, cover the picture up. In the grid underneath, see if you can redraw each caveman in its original pose. Once you're done, reveal the original picture and see if you were right!

The aim is to match the poses, not the exact drawings - you don't need to recreate the original art.

The first wheels were probably made of **solid wood** *rather than rounded stone, as is sometimes shown in cartoons. The oldest wheel ever found was discovered in Slovenia, and dates back over 5,000 years.*

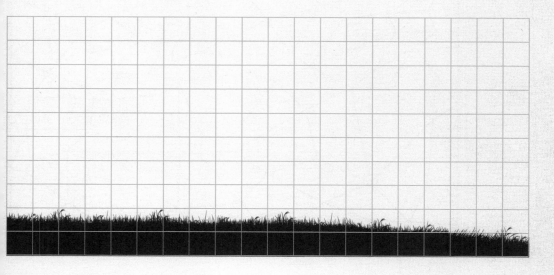

A CAVE OF COLOURS

The oldest-known **cave paintings** *can be found in France, and are over 40,000 years old.*

Many of our human ancestors lived in caves, which offered them protection from predators and the weather. Around the world, drawings have been discovered inside caves that have survived for thousands of years, and give us a glimpse of what life was like in these prehistoric homes.

Colour in the image below using the number key. What does your cave painting reveal?

KEY:
1 = light grey
2 = grey
3 = dark red

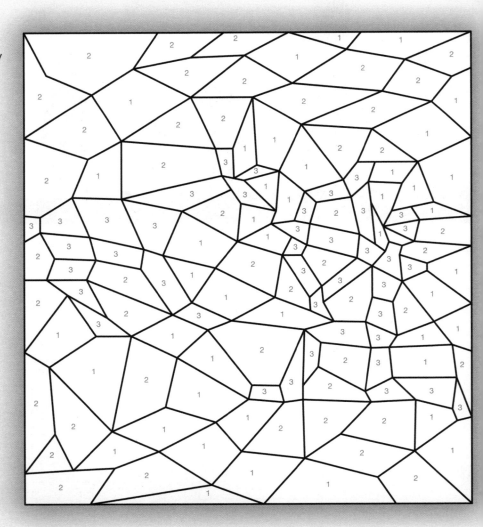

THE HANDS-ON APPROACH

The Cave of Hands is a famous Argentinian cave, known by the locals as Cueva de las Manos. Painted onto the walls are 9,000-year-old pictures of hands. It's thought that the people who made them blew paint at the walls through pipes and used their left hands as stencils to create the silhouettes.

Have a look at the pictures below. Can you match the five pairs of identical hands with each other?

TWISTED TONGUES

مرحبا

DID YOU KNOW?

There are currently around **7,000** different languages spoken in the world, although many are spoken by very few people and may not survive for much longer.

In the list below are some of the languages spoken around the world. But you might not recognise them - even if you speak them - because we've jumbled up the letters in their names. Can you unscramble their letters to reveal the real names? Ignore the spaces - they're just there for fun.

1. HID IN
2. AIR CAB
3. LEG SHIN
4. HAS SPIN
5. EARN OK
6. DRAIN MAN
7. WEARING ON
8. UPSET ROGUE

Once you've revealed the languages, can you guess which of them is the most widely-spoken?

Languages have family trees too. **"Romance"** languages, such as French, Spanish and Italian, are all descended from Latin, for example.

WRITING ON THE WALL

After humans developed language, they needed a way to record important things. Some of the first writing systems used a different picture for each word, instead of the letter-based alphabet that we use in English.

Imagine you're an archaeologist uncovering a brand-new alphabet inside an ancient tomb, and trying to work out what an ancient writer had to say. Can you crack the code using the symbols and key below in order to reveal a hidden message?

DID YOU KNOW?

The ancient Egyptians used a system of picture-words called **hieroglyphics**. Some hieroglyphics represented particular words, while others represented particular sounds.

THE CODE:

Key:

𓁹	Look	𓁷	That
𓀾	Mummy	𓀹	Is
𓈗	River	𓀠	Are
𓃂	Across	𓏥	Waking
𓃀	Help	𓅯	Swimming
𓆓	Up		

153

POINTED PAIRS

The first human weapons - arrows and spears - were made by sharpening flint stones and attaching them to sticks. Early humans used them both for hunting large animals and defending themselves.

Have a look at the flints on the left, and the weapons on the right, in the picture below. Can you work out which flint became which weapon? Draw a line between the matching pairs.

STAY OFF MY LAND!

After tens of thousands of years of hunting and gathering their food, human beings eventually began to settle in one place and grow their own food. In other words, they became farmers.

Imagine you're one of the very first farmers. You've planted some corn, but you have to find a way to stop wild animals eating it before you can harvest it. Can you draw a fence that joins all of the fence posts below in order to protect your crop from unwelcome visitors?

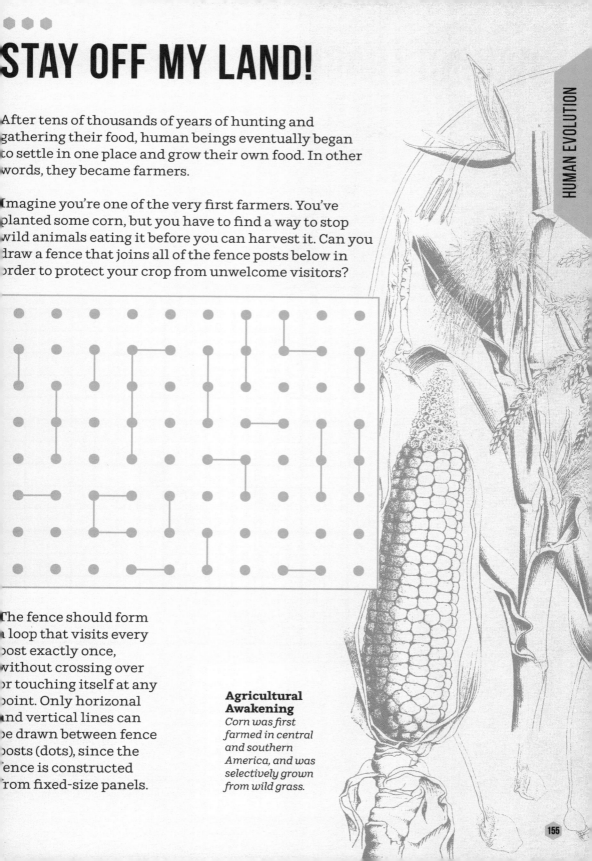

The fence should form a loop that visits every post exactly once, without crossing over or touching itself at any point. Only horizonal and vertical lines can be drawn between fence posts (dots), since the fence is constructed from fixed-size panels.

Agricultural Awakening
Corn was first farmed in central and southern America, and was selectively grown from wild grass.

MAKING TRACKS

A 15,000-year-old remnant, similar to the one hidden in this puzzle, was recently discovered **preserved** in rock in Chile.

Hidden in the grid below is something left behind from man's journey out of Africa. Can you reveal it by solving the clues? The clues provide, in reading order, the length of every run of consecutive shaded squares in each row and column. There must be a gap of at least one empty square between each run of shaded squares in the same row or column.

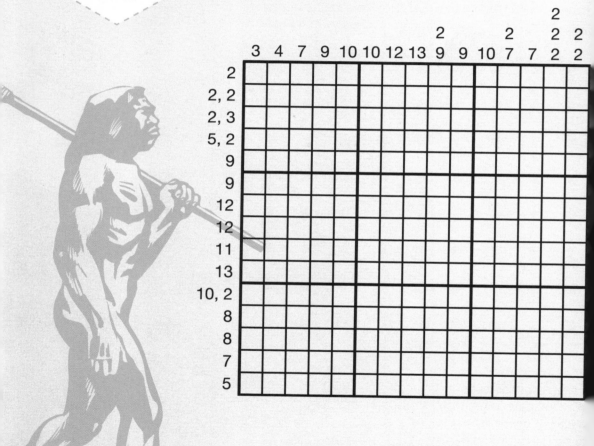

A TRICKY TRAIL

An ancient cave painting shows a muddle of tracks created by some early humans. Which of the four paths at the top of the cave leads to the wooly mammoth at the bottom?

The oldest-surviving map of the world is the **"Babylonian Map of the World"**. It was scratched into a clay tablet back in the sixth century BC.

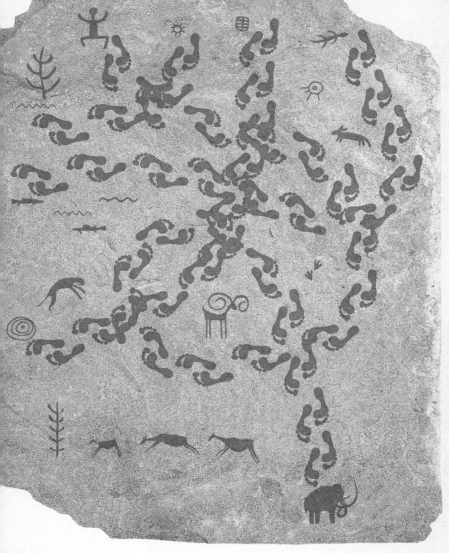

WONDERFUL WARDROBE

When humans first began to migrate around the world, they had to protect themselves from colder climates by making clothes. Fabrics were developed much later on with the invention of weaving, and dyes were created from plants and insects to give clothes bright colours.

The picture below has been left blank for you to draw and colour in some early clothes. Feel free to use your imagination - no one knows exactly what early people wore, so you can't go wrong!

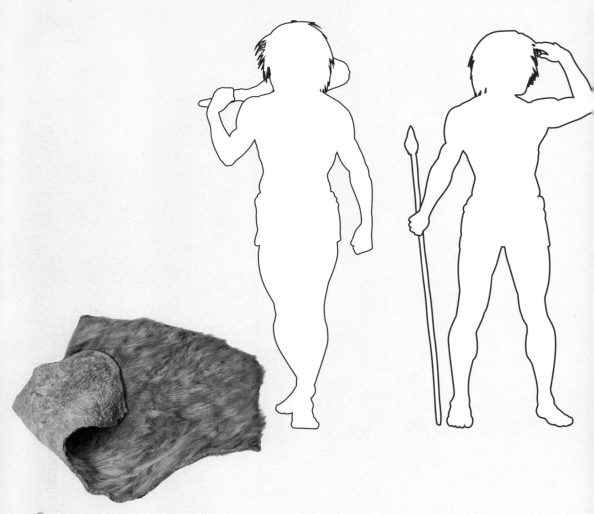

AN ARTIST'S EXPEDITION

Lapis lazuli is a bright blue rock which can be ground into a powder to make ultramarine, a natural dye. Ultramarine could then be mixed with other substances to make a blue paint, which was often kept for special uses due to its relative rarity and intense colour.

Imagine you're an artist looking for some *lapis lazuli* to grind up and use in your work. Can you make your way through the maze below to find this precious stone?

The world "ultramarine" comes from the Latin for **"beyond the sea"**.

THE CODED SECRET

Every plant and animal on this planet owes its existence to a special type of molecule known as DNA, which is short for deoxyribonucleic acid. DNA contains long chains of "instructions", which tell each cell how to grow and work. Lots and lots of cells grouped together make up the entire body of each plant or animal, with different types of cell doing different types of work.

For a long time, scientists were unable to work out the structure of DNA. They knew that once they unlocked it, they could start to examine the secret code that nature uses to create every living thing. Then, in 1952, scientists at Cambridge University finally unlocked the secret.

Key:

1 = white 5 = orange
2 = purple 6 = green
3 = pink 7 = yellow
4 = blue

DNA consists of a series of instructions called **"genes"** *that tell your body how to make the proteins that you need, such as insulin. You have around 20,000 different genes.*

Colour in the squares using the number key to the left to find out for yourself what the scientists James Watson and Francis Crick discovered.

1	2	2	2	1	1	1	1	1	1	1	1	1	1	1	1	1	1	1	1	1	3	3	3	1									
1	1	2	2	2	4	4	4	4	4	4	4	4	4	4	4	4	4	4	4	3	3	3	3	1									
1	1	2	2	2	2	4	4	4	4	4	4	4	4	4	4	4	4	3	3	3	3	1	1										
1	1	1	2	2	2	2	1	1	1	1	1	1	1	1	1	3	3	3	3	1	1	1											
1	1	1	1	2	2	2	2	1	1	1	1	1	1	1	1	3	3	3	3	1	1	1	1										
1	1	1	1	1	2	2	2	2	1	1	1	1	1	1	3	3	3	3	1	1	1	1	1										
1	1	1	1	1	1	2	2	2	2	1	1	3	3	3	3	1	1	1	1	1	1												
1	1	1	1	1	1	1	2	2	2	2	2	3	3	3	1	1	1	1	1	1	1												
1	1	1	1	1	1	1	1	2	2	2	2	2	3	3	1	1	1	1	1	1	1												
1	1	1	1	1	1	3	3	3	2	2	2	2	2	2	1	1	1	1	1	1	1												
1	1	1	1	3	3	3	3	3	3	3	1	2	2	2	2	2	2	1	1	1	1	1											
1	1	1	3	3	3	3	3	3	1	1	1	1	2	2	2	2	2	2	1	1	1	1											
1	1	1	3	3	3	3	1	1	1	1	1	1	1	2	2	2	2	2	2	1	1	1											
1	1	3	3	3	3	1	1	1	1	1	1	1	1	2	2	2	2	2	1	1	1												
1	1	3	3	3	3	5	5	5	5	5	5	5	5	5	5	5	2	2	2	2	1	1											
1	3	3	3	3	5	5	5	5	5	5	5	5	5	5	5	5	5	2	2	2	2	1											
1	3	3	3	1	1	1	1	1	1	1	1	1	1	1	1	1	1	1	1	2	2	2	2										
3	3	3	3	1	1	1	1	1	1	1	1	1	1	1	1	1	1	1	1	2	2	2	2										
3	3	3	6	6	6	6	6	6	6	6	6	6	6	6	6	6	6	6	6	6	6	2	2	2									
3	3	3	6	6	6	6	6	6	6	6	6	6	6	6	6	6	6	6	6	6	6	2	2	2									
3	3	3	1	1	1	1	1	1	1	1	1	1	1	1	1	1	1	1	1	1	1	2	2	2									
3	3	3	7	7	7	7	7	7	7	7	7	7	7	7	7	7	7	7	7	7	2	2	2										
3	3	3	7	7	7	7	7	7	7	7	7	7	7	7	7	7	7	7	7	7	2	2	2										
1	3	3	3	1	1	1	1	1	1	1	1	1	1	1	1	1	1	1	1	2	2	2	2										
1	3	3	3	1	1	1	1	1	1	1	1	1	1	1	1	1	1	1	2	2	2	2	1										
1	1	3	3	3	4	4	4	4	4	4	4	4	4	4	4	4	4	4	2	2	2	2	1										
1	1	3	3	3	3	4	4	4	4	4	4	4	4	4	4	4	4	2	2	2	2	1	1										
1	1	1	3	3	3	1	1	1	1	1	1	1	1	1	2	2	2	2	1	1	1												
1	1	1	3	3	3	3	1	1	1	1	1	1	1	2	2	2	2	1	1	1	1												
1	1	1	1	3	3	3	3	3	1	1	1	1	2	2	2	2	1	1	1	1	1												
1	1	1	1	1	3	3	3	3	3	1	1	1	2	2	2	2	1	1	1	1	1												
1	1	1	1	1	1	3	3	3	3	3	2	2	2	2	1	1	1	1	1	1	1												
1	1	1	1	1	1	1	3	3	3	3	3	2	1	1	1	1	1	1	1	1	1												
1	1	1	1	1	1	1	2	2	2	3	3	3	3	3	3	3	1	1	1	1	1												
1	1	1	1	1	1	2	2	2	2	2	1	1	3	3	3	3	3	1	1	1	1												
1	1	1	1	1	2	2	2	2	1	1	1	1	1	1	3	3	3	3	1	1	1												
1	1	1	2	2	2	2	1	1	1	1	1	1	1	1	1	3	3	3	3	1	1	1											
1	1	2	2	2	2	1	1	1	1	1	1	1	1	1	1	1	3	3	3	3	1	1											
1	1	2	2	2	5	5	5	5	5	5	5	5	5	5	5	5	5	3	3	3	1	1											
1	2	2	2	5	5	5	5	5	5	5	5	5	5	5	5	5	5	3	3	3	3	1											
1	2	2	2	1	1	1	1	1	1	1	1	1	1	1	1	1	1	1	3	3	3	1											
2	2	2	1	1	1	1	1	1	1	1	1	1	1	1	1	1	1	1	1	1	3	3	3										

MESSAGING MATHS

? Genes are grouped into chromosomes, and we have 46 chromosomes in almost every cell in our bodies. We get half of our chromosomes from our mother, and the other half from our father, which is why we share the characteristics of both of our parents. But how many chromosomes do we get from each parent individually?

? Human beings have around 20,000 genes, but a banana has roughly 150% of the number of genes that we do. So approximately how many genes does a banana have?

? Messages from the brain travel quickly to the rest of our body through our nerves. In fact, a message from the brain to a muscle can travel at almost 120 metres (393ft) per second. To give you an idea of how fast this is, can you work out how long it would take a nerve message to travel the length of a marathon? Assume a marathon is 42 kilometres (137,795ft) long in total.

SKELETON SORTING

Below is an image you might recognise - it's a human skeleton!

Unfortunately, some of the bones have been knocked out and are shown below. See if you can put them back in the right place by drawing lines to the suitable gaps in the skeleton.

The typical adult human has **206 bones** *in total.*

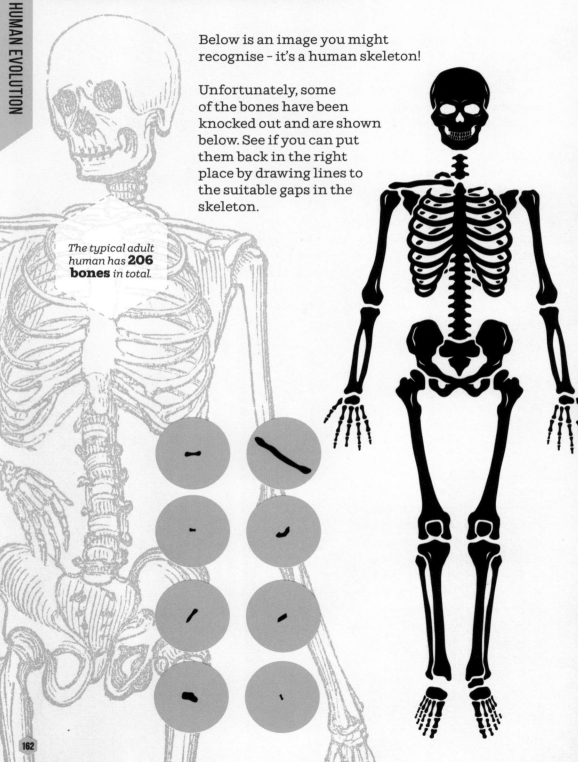

HUMAN BODY QUIZ

How much do you know about your own body?
Take this multiple-choice quiz to find out!

*The smallest bones in the body can be found inside your **ear**.*

? **What is the longest bone in your body?**
a) Femur
b) Tibia
c) Clavicle

? **How many teeth does the average adult human have?**
a) 26
b) 42
c) 32

? **What is the coloured part of your eye called?**
a) Iris
b) Retina
c) Cornea

? **Where in your body would you find alveoli?**
a) Small intestine
b) Lungs
c) Gall bladder

? **The human body has a surprisingly large number of muscles, many of which are tiny and move substances around the body. But roughly how many skeletal muscles – those that move the skeleton around – do we have?**
a) 150
b) 650
c) 1,150

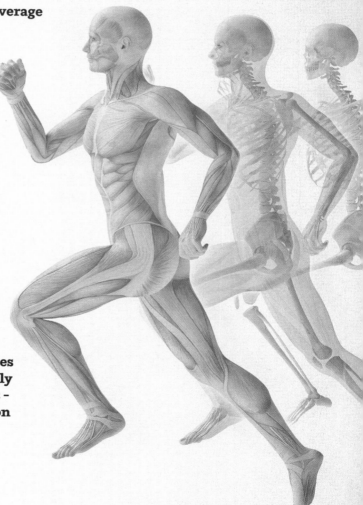

PARALLEL PUZZLE

Your brain can do many amazing things, and it does most of them without you needing to be consciously aware of them. For example, you can look at a face and recognise it immediately as a face without any extra effort – you don't need to think, "that looks like an eye, and maybe that's a nose…".

Sometimes the brain's automatic visual processing can be tricked with pictures that have been drawn to deliberately confuse it. For example, take a look at the optical illusion picture below. Are the long red and purple lines parallel, or do they run in different directions?

Most adult brains weigh about 1.3kg (2.9lbs) – the same as an average **pineapple**.

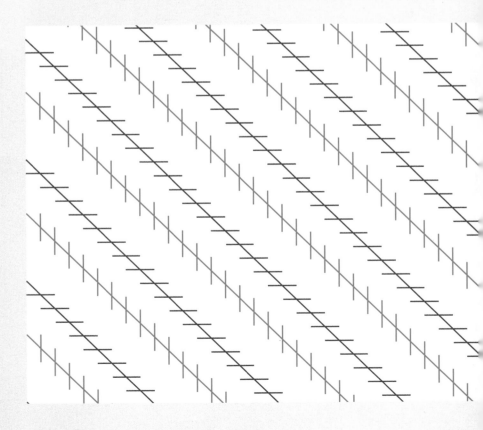

MIND-BENDING MAGIC

Here's another optical illusion. Look at the light-blue lines in the grid below. Do they form a perfect grid, or are some of the squares distorted?

The human brain is **73% water** *- and your body overall is about 60% water. This is one reason why it's so important to keep well-hydrated.*

VIRUSES VERSUS VACCINES

Viruses make us ill by reproducing in large enough quantities that they interrupt our normal bodily functions.

See if you can reduce the threat of the viruses in the puzzle below by keeping them apart. Place just one virus into every fenced-off region of the grid. There should be only one virus in each row and each column, and they can't be in touching squares - not even diagonally. One is already in place for you.

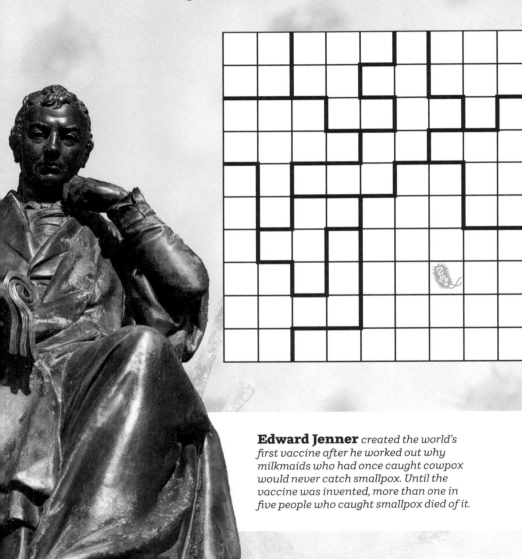

Edward Jenner created the world's first vaccine after he worked out why milkmaids who had once caught cowpox would never catch smallpox. Until the vaccine was invented, more than one in five people who caught smallpox died of it.

CODE-BREAKING CONUNDRUM

Human beings are living longer than ever before, largely because modern medicine is working to crack the codes behind diseases that make us unwell.

Can you also crack the code in this grid? All you need to do is place numbers from 1 up to the size of the region into each bold-lined region. For example, if a region contains 5 squares, then you must place 1 to 5 into it. Identical numbers can't touch – not even diagonally.

1	2			2	3		1
		1			5	2	
1		5					5
	3		6				4
4				5		3	
6					1		2
	4	3			6		
3		1	2			5	2

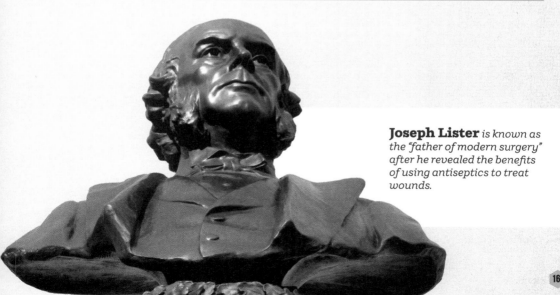

Joseph Lister *is known as the "father of modern surgery" after he revealed the benefits of using antiseptics to treat wounds.*

● ● ●
READY, SET, SCIENCE!

The goal of science is to build on the knowledge we already have about the world, and to explore topics that are still unknown to us. Scientists create a theory about how something might work, and then test it to see if their theory is correct. In a sense, it's like solving a puzzle - although some of the puzzles are incredibly complicated, and take the combined work of many people over many years to solve!

The two puzzles on these pages might require you to test out some theories of your own before you can solve them. Don't worry if your prediction doesn't work first time - not all theories do!

DID YOU KNOW?

The word science comes from the Latin **scientia**, meaning "knowledge".

Can you draw along some of the dashed grid lines, so that every number ends up contained within a solid-lined square or a rectangle? Each square or rectangle must contain the number of dashed-line grid squares indicated by its number, so a "6" must be within a 1x6, 2x3, 3x2 or 6x1 rectangle.

Each number can only appear within one solid-lined square or rectangle, and each dashed-line grid square is contained within exactly one solid-lined shape.

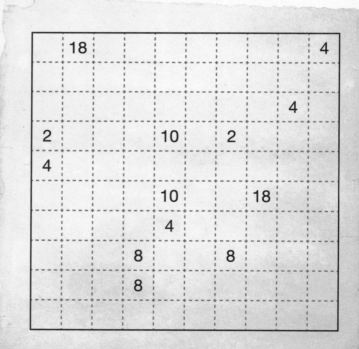

EXPERIMENTAL CONNECTIONS

Often a scientific theory arises from connecting together many smaller, separate observations.

In this puzzle, see if you can connect together each pair of identical shapes with paths which do not overlap. Each square must have no more than one path passing through it. The paths cannot cross over, and no more than one path can enter any square.

The history of the word **"puzzle"** is a puzzle in itself, since nobody is quite sure where it comes from!

Sir Richard Owen was an English biologist who helped found the Natural History Museum, London, and coined the name "dinosaur"!

EVOLVED

Congratulations! You've now followed the journey of humanity, from single cell to great ape and on to the modern human. But were you paying attention? See if you can answer the following quiz questions using the knowledge gained from the previous pages.

? Who discovered the antibiotic penicillin?
a) Joseph Lister
b) Alexander Fleming
c) Florence Nightingale

? Who achieved fame by describing the theory of evolution?
a) Charles Darwin
b) Marie Curie
c) Albert Einstein

? What type of stone was used to make early arrows and spears?
a) Flint
b) Sandstone
c) Chalk

? What is the "Smilodon", an extinct animal, better known as?
a) Woolly mammoth
b) Neanderthal
c) Sabre-toothed tiger

? Where could you find the Cave of Hands, full of ancient cave paintings?
a) Chile
b) Argentina
c) Mexico

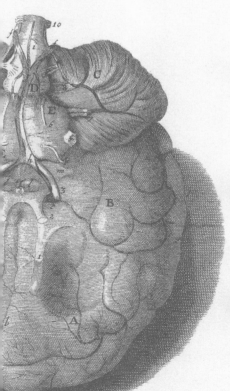

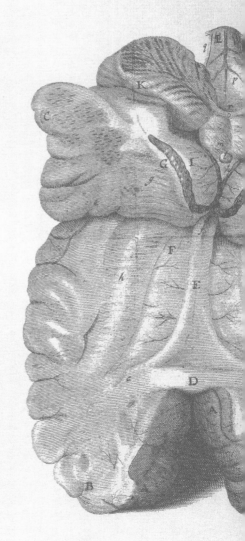

? **What is carmine, made from crushed insect shells, used for?**
a) An antiseptic
b) Food colouring
c) Building houses

? **Which rare stone is used to make the pigment ultramarine?**
a) Lapis lazuli
b) Diamond
c) Malachite

? **What is the name of the pictorial writing system used by the ancient Egyptians?**
a) Cuneiform
b) Runes
c) Hieroglyphics

? **How many bones are there in the average human body?**
a) 206
b) 428
c) 150

? **Who created the smallpox vaccine?**
a) Edward Jenner
b) Francis Crick
c) Alan Turing

CHAPTER 6:
THE NATURAL WORLD

WHAT IS THE NATURAL WORLD?

It's all around you! The ground beneath your feet, the air we breathe and the weather outside are all part of the natural world, as are all of the animals, plants and everything else not made by humans.

Natural disasters are part of the natural world too. Weather events, such as hurricanes and droughts, can cause damage to buildings and habitats, and geological disasters, such as earthquakes and volcanic eruptions, can change the shape of Earth's surface.

A Family Affair

Without plants, we wouldn't be able to exist on Earth. They take carbon dioxide out of the air and turn it back into oxygen, and they form the basis of the food chain on which we rely.

DID YOU KNOW?

Earth formed over 4.5 billion years ago.

In the list to the right, can you match the foods and flowers on the right with their plant family on the left? Use guesswork if you aren't sure, then check the solutions at the back to see how you did. Also, see if you can find all ten of the plant family names in the wordsearch on the opposite page.

PLANT FAMILY	FLOWER OR FOOD
APIACEAE	ROSE
FABACEAE	GRAPE
LAURACEAE	POTATO
LILIACEAE	VIOLET
POACEAE	PEA
ROSACEAE	CELERY
RUTACEAE	ORANGE
SOLANACEAE	AVOCADO
VITACEAE	GRASS
VIOLACEAE	LILY

Can you find the plant family names in the wordsearch?

```
A E L C U E R I A A R C C F I
R O S A C E A E A A E C A L B
V A L A A A A L A E U B A A E
A N O L A O E C A C A E E U A
A I V A I B E E E C C A E E C
E F I A T L C A E A E E A B S
A E A E E A I A E C E E S O P
L E A E L E E A A C C C L C A
N A E O R C E I C A A A A I A
L A I E C E P C T E N R C O E
I V E O O A I I E A A P U L P
F E A A N S V A C S N E A A I
R U T A C E A E A R P C E L L
C A E A A E A A L A E E E E E
C I E A C E U L A L A A A E A
```

SCALING NEW HEIGHTS

Here are five famous mountains and their associated heights:

DID YOU KNOW?

Mount Everest is the world's tallest mountain.

5 – MOUNT EVEREST
8,848m (29,030ft)

4 – K2
8,611m (28,250ft)

1 – TABLE MOUNTAIN
1,085m (3,558ft)

2 – MONT BLANC
4,810m (15,780ft)

3 – KILIMANJARO
5,895m (19,340ft)

Can you place all of the mountains (represented by the numbers 1-5 as labelled above) into the grid on the left, so that one of each mountain is placed into each row and column? This means that each mountain will be placed a total of five times.

Arrows between some pairs of squares point to the square which contains the shorter of the two mountains in that pair of squares.

RACE TO THE TOP

Can you help the mountaineer find a path all the way to the top of Mount Everest? Colour in the flag on top when you're done!

In 1953, **Tenzing Norgay** and **Sir Edmund Hillary** became the first people to climb Mount Everest.

The **Himalayan** mountain range, where Mount Everest is located, is one of the youngest mountain ranges. It started to form "only" 50 million years ago.

VOLATILE EARTH

The coastal area around the Pacific Ocean is known as the **"ring of fire"**, *due to its frequent geological activity.*

Occasionally, molten rock and metal from beneath Earth's crust break through the surface in an explosion that throws super-hot lava into the air. Do you know what type of event this is? Colour in the sections using the number key below to find out, and reveal this dramatic geological phenomenon.

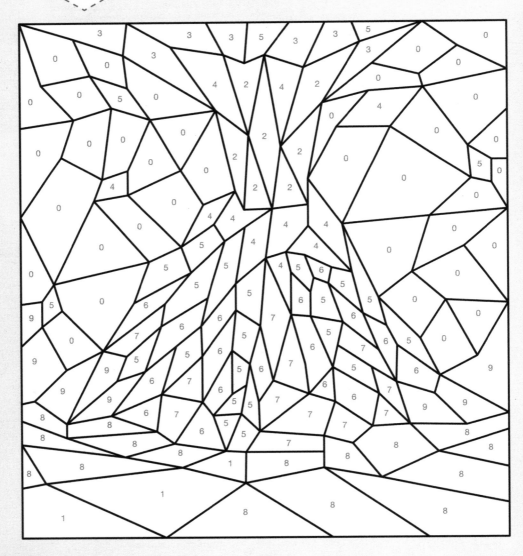

KEY:

1 = red **3** = grey **5** = orange **7** = brown **9** = dark green

2 = light grey **4** = yellow **6** = light brown **8** = green **0** = blue

JIGSAW PLATES

Earth's crust isn't one smooth surface – it's made up of separate pieces called tectonic plates, which fit together like an enormous jigsaw. Earthquakes happen when the edges of tectonic plates move against one another, and the resulting forces are so powerful that they make the ground shake.

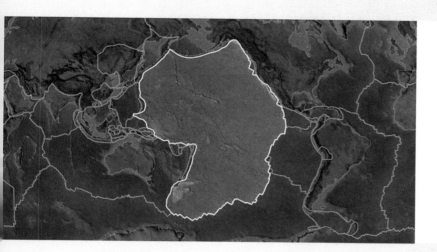

*The largest tectonic plate is the **Pacific Plate**, covering the area beneath the Pacific Ocean.*

See if you can draw along the lines in the grid to the left to divide the grid into a set of rectangular and square tectonic plates of your own, so that each plate contains a single number. That number must be equal to the total number of grid squares that it covers. Plates can't overlap, and all grid squares must be covered by a plate.

BEFORE AND AFTER

Have a look at these two pictures of a kitchen cupboard. On the left is the cupboard before an earthquake, and on the right is what it might look like after. Can you spot five differences between them?

In some countries, such as Chile and Japan, earthquakes are a common part of life. Japan is hit by around **1,500 earthquakes** *every year - although some are so small you can barely feel them.*

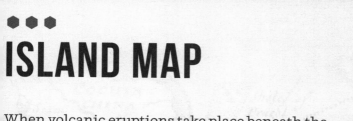

ISLAND MAP

When volcanic eruptions take place beneath the surface of the ocean, sometimes the hot lava cools to create a new island, or extra land on an existing island. This process happens continually around Hawaii, for example.

The small Japanese island of **Nishinoshima** *has been growing sporadically since 1974, when a dormant volcano suddenly woke up after a 10,000-year nap!*

Imagine you're a cartographer who has to map out a new island that's just formed, and your first task is to draw its outline. You've received information from some specialist instruments which allow you to work out the shape. Draw it by connecting some of the dots in the puzzle above so that each numbered square forms the island's outline. When drawing the outline, each number should have the specified number of line segments passing alongside it. Dots can only be joined by horizontal or vertical lines, and the loop cannot touch, cross or overlap itself at any point.

● ● ●

WINDY WEATHER

Wind speed is measured in knots. The instruments that measure wind speed are known as anemometers (left).

You've probably seen weather maps covered in arrows, showing the direction and speed of the wind.

In the simpler "map" (or grid) below, wind only blows horizontally or vertically, and it's up to you to work out which by drawing either a horizontal or vertical line in each empty square.

Numbers in the grid reveal the total length of the horizontal or vertical lines that join to their square, measured in grid squares. Lines that touch multiple numbers count towards the total for all the numbers they touch.

A

NORTH
AMERICA

SOUTH
AMERICA

B

	3			7		
		5				4
3	3					
					3	2
2			4			
		8			4	

WINDS OF THE WORLD

Have a look at the map below. The arrows show the direction of some famous winds that regularly appear in these areas, but their names are listed separately. Can you match each of the names to the corresponding wind on the map? If there are any that you recognise, start with those.

The Beaufort scale is used to describe wind and sea conditions, using a scale from 1 to 12, where 1 is complete calm and 12 is a hurricane.

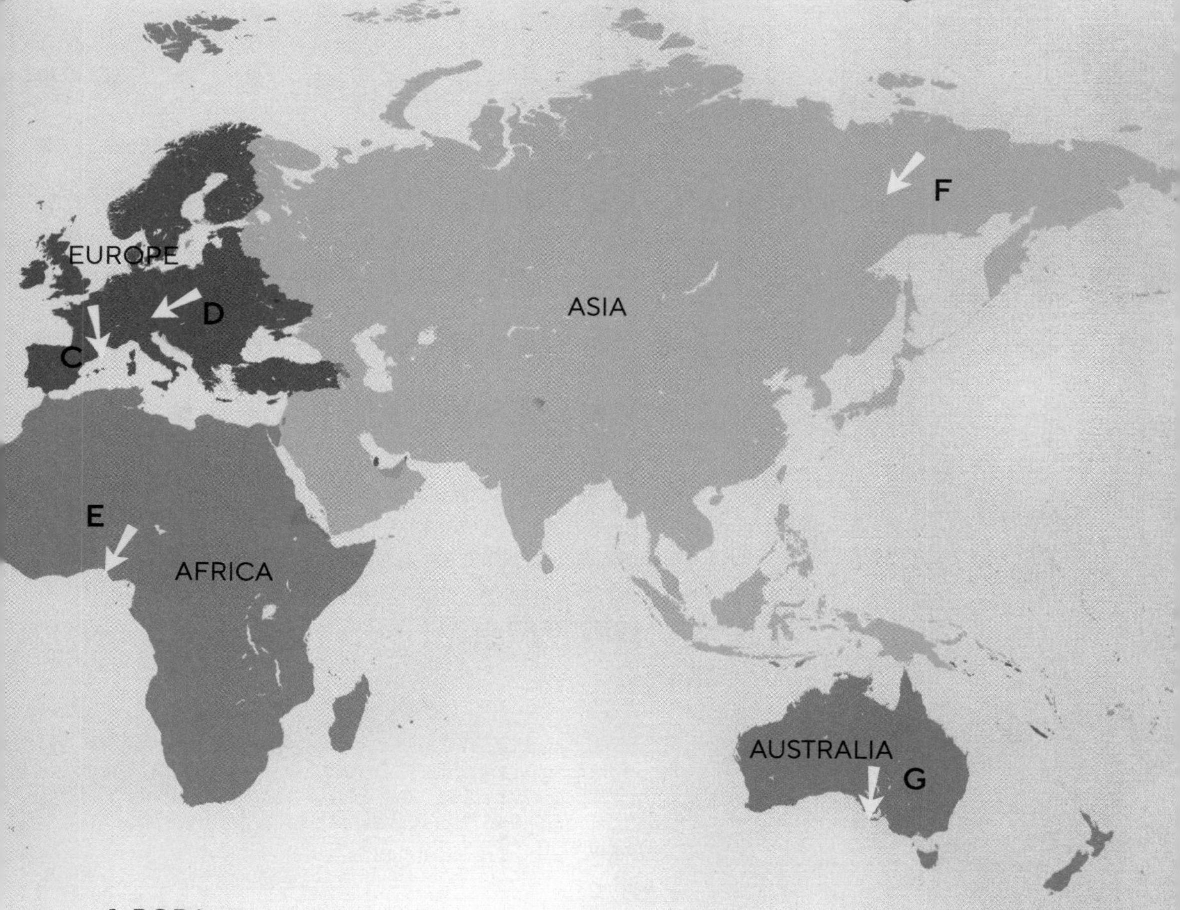

EUROPE

D

C

ASIA

F

E

AFRICA

AUSTRALIA

G

1. BORA
2. BRICKFIELDER
3. BURAN
4. CHINOOK
5. HARMATTAN
6. MISTRAL
7. PAMPERO

●●● FIREBREAKS

Forest fires can be contained by creating "firebreaks", which are large ditches or paths that run across land and are wide enough that a fire can't jump across. These are constructed in advance of fires as a precaution, in case the land should burn.

*Some trees are well adapted to survive forest fires. **Giant sequoias** (below) have thick fire-resistant bark, and **cypress trees** store so much water in their needles and trunks that it's difficult for fires to kill them.*

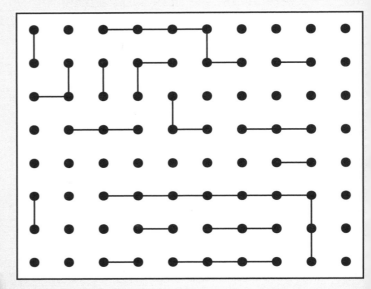

Create your own firebreak in the grid above by joining all of the dots together to form a single loop. You can only use horizontal or vertical lines, and your loop cannot cross over or touch itself. Some of the loop has already been drawn.

*In some areas of the world, the land regularly catches fire as part of its natural cycle. In fact, some plants – like the **Banksia** in Australia – rely on the heat to open their seed pods, and the fire-cleared ground to help grow without competition.*

TORNADO TROUBLE

A tornado is a powerful wind that travels in a funnel-shaped, spinning cloud, destroying everything in its path. Due to their shape, tornadoes are sometimes also known as twisters, and they are common in central USA, an area known as Tornado Alley.

Imagine you've just come out of a tornado shelter – after the all-clear signal – to find that your bicycle has blown away. Can you find your way through the centre of the maze and out the other side to discover where it's ended up?

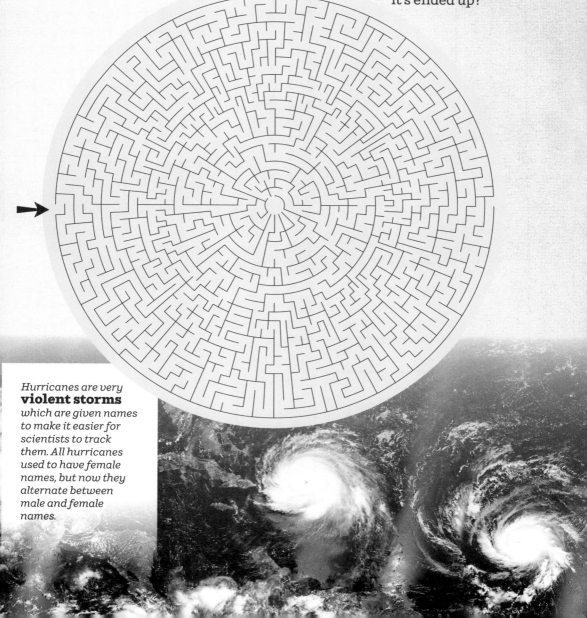

Hurricanes are very **violent storms** *which are given names to make it easier for scientists to track them. All hurricanes used to have female names, but now they alternate between male and female names.*

THE WATER CYCLE

The water on Earth is re-used in a continual loop, known as the water cycle. Warm water rises from the sea to form clouds, and this water later falls as rain, eventually making its way back to the sea via streams and rivers to start the cycle all over again.

Can you create a water cycle of your own? Enter the numbers 1, 2 and 3 into some of the squares on the left, so that as you trace your way around the spiral from the outside inwards, you read 1, 2, 3, 1, 2, 3, etc. Each number must appear exactly once in each row and column, which means that not every square will have a number in it.

A FORCE OF NATURE

The force of water cascading over a waterfall will erode the rock at the bottom of the fall over time. For tall, powerful falls, this can create large pools. In the puzzle below, use the numeric clues to work out where the water is, and shade the squares that contain water. All the water in each connected area must pool as it would in real life, so water must fill an area from bottom to top, not from top to bottom. Water does not flow through bold-lined walls, however. Numbers outside the grid reveal how many squares contain water in each row and column.

The world's tallest waterfall is **Angel Falls** in Venezuela, at 979m (3211ft) tall.

The puzzle grid has the following clues:

Row clues (top to bottom): 1, 5, 6, 6, 6, 4, 6

Column clues (left to right): 4, 5, 4, 5, 5, 5, 6

Iguazu Falls, found on the border between Brazil and Argentina, is the largest system of waterfalls in the world.

A FOOL'S GAME

The mineral you see in the pictures below is called pyrite, but it's also known as "fool's gold" because of its metallic yellow colouring that makes the unwary mistake it for actual gold.

Look closely at the two pictures. Can you spot twelve differences between them?

Pyrite is named after the Greek word for **fire**. Pyrite crystals grow naturally in cubes – just like grains of salt.

HIDDEN TREASURES

Buried in the grid below are some rare and valuable materials which can be found underground. Colour in the squares according to the number key to reveal the precious finds.

The largest diamond ever found was the **Cullinan Diamond**, *discovered in South Africa in 1905.*

KEY:

1 = white
2 = yellow
3 = purple
4 = black
5 = pink
6 = red
7 = orange
8 = blue
9 = light blue
0 = dark green
A = green

```
1 1 2 2 3 2 2 2 2 1 1 2 4 4 2 2 2 2 2 2 2 2
1 2 2 3 5 3 2 2 1 1 2 4 6 7 4 2 2 2 2 2 2 2
2 2 3 6 5 5 5 3 1 1 2 4 6 6 1 7 4 2 2 2 2 1 1
2 3 6 6 3 5 5 3 2 2 4 6 6 6 6 4 2 2 2 1 1 2
3 6 6 3 6 3 5 1 3 2 2 4 6 6 4 2 2 1 1 1 2 2
3 6 3 6 6 5 3 5 3 2 2 2 4 4 2 1 1 1 2 2 2 2
3 6 3 6 6 5 3 5 3 2 2 2 2 1 1 1 2 2 2 2 2 2
3 6 3 6 6 5 3 5 3 2 1 1 1 2 4 4 2 2 2 2 1 1
3 6 3 6 6 5 3 5 3 2 1 1 2 2 4 8 9 4 2 1 1 1
3 6 3 6 6 6 3 5 3 1 1 2 2 4 8 4 4 4 9 4 1 2 2
3 6 6 3 6 3 6 6 3 2 2 2 4 8 4 8 4 8 9 4 2 2
2 3 6 6 3 6 6 3 2 2 2 4 8 8 4 8 4 8 4 9 9 4 2
2 2 3 6 6 6 3 2 2 2 4 3 8 4 8 8 8 8 4 9 1 4
2 2 2 3 6 3 2 2 2 2 4 8 4 8 8 8 9 4 1 9 4
2 2 1 1 3 2 2 2 2 2 4 8 3 4 8 8 8 9 4 9 9 4
2 1 1 2 2 2 2 1 1 1 4 8 3 4 8 9 8 9 4 9 9 4
1 1 2 2 2 2 1 1 2 2 4 8 3 4 8 9 9 9 4 9 9 4
2 2 2 2 2 1 1 2 2 4 8 3 4 9 9 8 9 4 9 9 4
2 2 3 3 3 3 3 4 2 2 4 8 3 4 9 8 8 9 4 9 9 4
2 3 6 6 6 6 5 3 4 2 4 3 3 4 8 8 9 4 9 9 4
2 3 3 3 6 3 3 3 3 2 4 3 4 3 4 8 8 9 4 9 9 4
2 6 3 3 6 3 3 5 3 2 4 3 3 4 8 9 9 9 4 9 9 4
2 2 6 3 6 3 5 3 2 2 4 3 3 4 8 9 9 9 4 9 9 4
1 1 3 6 6 5 3 4 2 2 4 8 3 4 9 9 8 9 4 9 9 4
1 2 2 3 6 3 4 2 2 2 4 8 3 4 9 8 8 9 4 9 9 4
2 2 2 2 3 4 2 1 1 1 4 8 3 4 8 8 8 9 4 9 9 4
2 2 2 2 2 2 1 1 2 2 4 8 3 4 8 8 9 8 4 9 9 4
2 2 2 1 1 1 1 2 2 4 8 3 4 8 9 9 8 4 8 9 4
1 1 1 1 2 2 2 2 2 2 4 3 3 4 8 8 4 8 8 4 2
1 2 0 0 0 0 0 0 0 2 2 2 4 3 4 8 8 4 8 4 2 2
2 0 A A A 2 A A 2 0 2 2 2 4 8 4 4 8 4 2 2 2
0 A A 0 0 0 0 0 1 2 0 2 2 2 4 8 8 4 2 2 2 2
0 A 0 A A 2 A 2 0 A 0 2 2 2 1 4 4 2 2 2 2 1
0 A 0 A A A A A 0 2 0 2 2 1 1 2 2 2 2 1 1 1
0 A 0 A A A A A 0 2 0 A 0 1 1 1 2 2 2 1 1 2 2
0 A 0 A A A A A 0 2 0 1 1 1 2 2 2 2 1 1 2 2
0 A 0 A A A A A 0 2 0 1 2 2 2 2 2 1 1 2 2 2
0 A 0 A A A A 2 0 2 0 2 2 2 2 2 1 1 2 2 2 2
0 A A 0 0 0 0 0 A 2 0 2 2 2 2 1 1 2 2 2 2 1
2 0 A A A A A A A 0 2 2 2 1 1 1 2 2 2 1 1 1
2 2 0 0 0 0 0 0 0 0 2 2 2 1 1 2 2 2 2 2 1 1 2
```

WHAT'S MINE IS MINE

When diamonds are found underground, they look more like colourful rocks than precious jewels. They need to be cut and polished to make them into the sparkly gems we might recognise.

Imagine the grid below is a diamond mine. Can you locate all of the diamonds? They are contained in some of the empty squares, with no more than one diamond per square. The numbers tell you how many diamonds there are in total in the squares touching each numbered square, including diagonally.

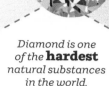

Diamond is one of the **hardest** natural substances in the world.

		2	3				1
3	3				4	3	
						2	
2		2					1
	3		3		2	2	
2		3		2			1
	2		2			4	
1				3			1

A CUNNING CARNIVORE

Plants make their own food using the sun's rays in a process called photosynthesis. It's not quite enough for some plants, however, who have come up with some unusual ways of obtaining extra nutrients!

Join the dots in increasing numerical order to reveal a dangerous-looking plant. Start at 1 and continue all the way up to 64. What do you reveal?

BUSY BEES

Plants are able to reproduce by making pollen, which insects then spread as they travel from plant to plant. Bees in particular are vital to the world's ecosystem, as they gather nectar from flowers and pollinate many other plants in the process too.

Can you map out a honeybee's many flight paths between the flowering plants below? Each of the circles in the puzzle represents a flower, and the number on each flower tells you exactly how many flight paths connect to each flower. Draw in the flight paths using horizontal or vertical lines that join from one flower to another, without crossing over another path or over another flower.

The **Rafflesia arnoldii**, also known as the corpse flower, smells very unpleasantly like rotting flesh. Despite this, it is one of the three national flowers of its native Indonesia.

Once done, you must be able to travel from any flower to any other by using the paths. No more than one path can join any given pair of flowers.

BLOOMS AND BLOSSOMS

DID YOU KNOW?

A piece of **broccoli** is actually made up of lots and lots of tiny flower heads.

The flowers of the world come in many different sizes, shapes and colours.

Start by colouring in the picture below as you choose. Then, if you wish, you could try drawing in some extra flowers of your own, too.

MIXED-UP MEADOW

Listed below are the names of some flowers that you might find growing in a garden - except that their letters have been scrambled.

Can you unscramble the letters to reveal each bloom? Ignore any spaces in the scrambled version.

1. SORE
2. IS DAY
3. UPLIT
4. IF OLD FAD
5. LULL BEEB
6. ROWS POND
7. AN IDLE DON
8. TUB PER CUT

There is no scientific group known as **"weeds"** *- it's just the name given to unwanted flowers.*

AGEING ARITHMETIC

For every year of a tree's life, a ring is added to the centre of its trunk. If you cut a tree down, you can count the rings inside the trunk to work out how old it was.

Have a look at the segments of the four tree trunks shown below. Can you work out which tree is the oldest?

A giant sequoia known as **General Sherman** *is the largest living tree on Earth, in terms of its total volume. It can be found in Sequoia National Park in California, and is over 2,000 years old.*

GENERAL SHERMAN

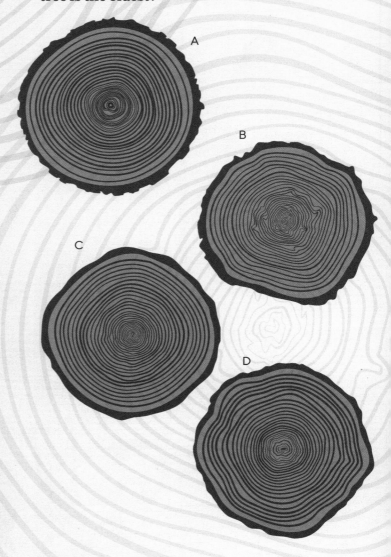

A

B

C

D

TREES BY THE NUMBERS

? The fastest-growing plant is bamboo, growing up to 90cm (3ft) in a single day! How much taller could it grow in a week?

? The world's tallest tree has been named Hyperion, and is a coastal redwood tree that is 380 feet (115m) tall. How many people, would have to stand on top of one other to be as tall as Hyperion? Assume that each person is 6 feet (1.8m) tall.

? The oldest living tree is a bristlecone pine known as Methuselah, which was estimated to be 4,850 years old in 2019. If that estimate was correct, in what year did the tree start to grow?

MICROSCOPIC MUSHROOMS

Fungi
are neither plants nor animals, but belong in a scientific kingdom of their own.

When we see mushrooms above ground, they are often connected to a large, underground fungus system that is hidden beneath. In fact, the largest living organism in the world is not a blue whale, but a fungus! It's a honey fungus found in the Blue Mountains of Oregon, which is connected underground into an enormous organism that's linked with microscopic threads called mycelia.

Create your own fungus links in the puzzle below by drawing paths to join each pair of identical mushrooms. Each square must have no more than one path passing through it. The paths cannot cross over, and no more than one path can enter any square.

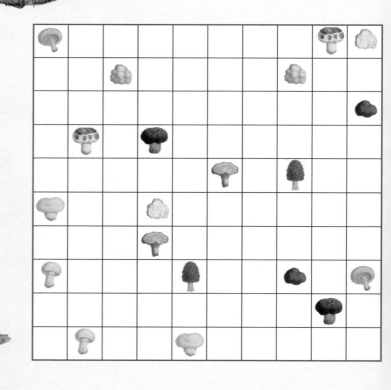

· · ·

FUN FUNGI

What do jellyfish, fireflies and mushrooms all have in common? Some of their species glow in the dark! For example, some fungi species produce their own bioluminescent light, which they use to attract insects.

See if you can light up the puzzle by adding your own glowing mushrooms to it, according to the rules below.

KEY:

- You can add a mushroom to any empty square, but not a shaded one.
- Light shines out of every mushroom in both horizontal and vertical directions along the same row and column. Light travels until it reaches either the edge of the grid or a shaded square.
- Some shaded squares have numbers on them. This exact number of mushrooms must be placed in the touching squares (left/right/up/down, but not including diagonally) – no more, and no less.
- Every unshaded square of the grid must be lit by at least one mushroom.
- No mushroom can shine on any other mushroom.

A NATURAL HISTORY

*The further you go underground, the hotter the temperature gets. This is because you're getting closer to Earth's **molten core**!*

Much of what we have discovered about the history of the natural world has come from looking beneath our feet, where we have discovered fossils, ancient river courses, precious gems and so much more. Without looking underground, many pieces of the world's natural history might have been lost.

Test your own memory for natural history by looking closely at the picture below – and cover over the picture on the opposite page.

You'll see lots of things that you might have learned about already in this book, buried underground. Once you've memorised where each object is, cover over the picture on the left and see if you can identify which objects have changed or vanished in the version of the picture on the opposite page. Once you've finished, check back to see if you were right. Happy digging!

The oldest fossils ever found contained evidence of creatures that lived over **3 billion years ago**.

NATURAL WORLD QUIZ

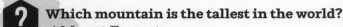

Congratulations! If you've made it this far, you must be a true Natural History explorer. But were you paying attention in this chapter? Test your knowledge to see what you've learned about the natural world:

? **Which mountain is the tallest in the world?**
a) Mount Everest
b) Kilimanjaro
c) Table Mountain

? **Which of the following are pieces of Earth's crust, which fit together like a giant jigsaw?**
a) Pacific pieces
b) Tectonic plates
c) Earthquake plates

? **Whereabouts in the world would you find a Brickfielder wind?**
a) Australia
b) Russia
c) Canada

? **What is the name of a device used to measure wind speed?**
a) Weather vane
b) Beaufort meter
c) Anemometer

? **What is pyrite better known as?**
a) Digger's gold
b) Fool's gold
c) Miner's gold

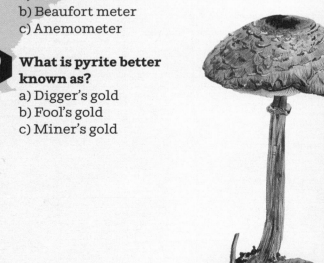

? **Which is the world's tallest waterfall?**
a) Angel Falls, Venezuela
b) Seven Waterfalls, Bolivia
c) Iguazu Falls, Brazil

? **In what country was the largest-ever diamond found?**
a) Australia
b) New Zealand
c) South Africa

? **What is the name for the process whereby plants make their food from the sun's energy?**
a) Bioluminescence
b) Telekinesis
c) Photosynthesis

? **What name has been given to the world's tallest tree?**
a) General Sherman
b) Hyperion
c) Methuselah

? **What does a mycologist study?**
a) Fungi
b) Carnivorous plants
c) Fruit

SOLUTIONS

Pages 10-11
The Animal Kingdom

The animals are as follows:

COMMON NAME	BINOMIAL NAME
ARCTIC HARE	LEPUS ARCTICUS
ASIAN ELEPHANT	ELEPHAS MAXIMUS
ATLANTIC SALMON	SALMO SALAR
BARN OWL	TYTO ALBA
BISON	BISON BISON
CAT	FELIS CATUS
COW	BOS TAURUS
GIANT CLAM	TRIDACNA GIGAS
GREY WOLF	CANIS LUPUS
HUMAN	HOMO SAPIENS
LION	PANTHERA LEO
LLAMA	LAMA GLAMA
LYNX	LYNX LYNX
MONARCH BUTTERFLY	DANAUS PLEXIPPUS
POLAR BEAR	URSUS MARITIMUS
WILD HORSE	EQUUS FERUS

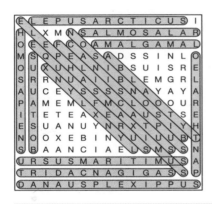

Page 12
Matching Antlers

Page 13
Primate Living

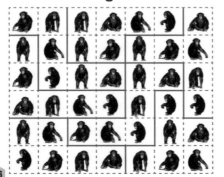

Page 15
Large Animals

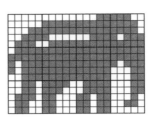

Page 16
Find the Snake

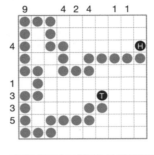

Page 17
A Square Disguise

Page 18
Flight of the Bumblebee

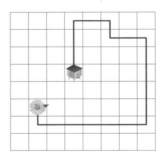

Page 19
Butterfly Bias

Pages 20-21
Beautiful Beetles

Page 22
Penguin Pairs

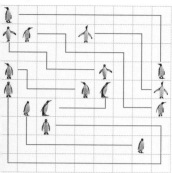

Page 26
Jungle Colour

A red-eyed tree frog.

Page 27
Life Cycle of Frogs

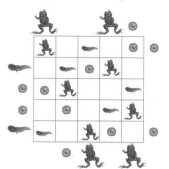

SOLUTIONS

Page 23
Split Eggs

Pages 28-29
Night-time Creatures
11.

Page 24
Birdwatcher's Paradise

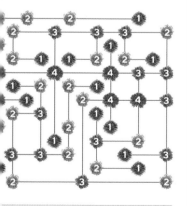

Page 30
Hidden Animals

		3		●	3	2
●	6	●	●	6	●	●
●	●	4	●	●	●	●
	4			4		2
●		●		●	2	
2		2	4	2		●
●	2	●		●	2	1

Page 31
Night-time Mystery

The picture is of a sugar glider, a type of possum belonging to the marsupial family.

Page 25
Feathered Facts

Twice as big.
72,500 times heavier; because the bee hummingbird is so small, it could be mistaken for a bee.
1.6kg (3½lbs); 800 times heavier.
15,000 breaths.

Page 32
Habitat Match-up

The animals are as follows:

HABITAT	ANIMAL
AMAZON RAINFOREST	BLUE POISON DART FROG
ANTARCTIC	PENGUIN
CAVE	BAT
DEEP OCEAN	VAMPIRE SQUID
DESERT	SCORPION
ROCK POOL	HERMIT CRAB
SAVANNAH	ZEBRA
WOODLAND	HEDGEHOG

Page 33
Penguin Protection

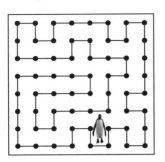

Page 34
Hidden in Plain Sight

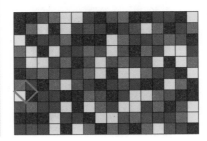

Page 35
Spider's Web

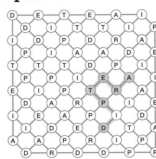

Page 36
Animal Orderings

1 Blue whale
140,000kg (22,000st).
2 African bush elephant
6,000kg (950st).
3 Hippopotamus
1,600kg (250st).
4 Polar bear 450kg (70st).
5 Emu 35kg (5.5st).

1 Javan rhino
(Critically Endangered).
2 Chimpanzee (Endangered).
3 Great white shark
(Vulnerable).
4 Jaguar (Near Threatened).
5 Bottlenose dolphin
(Least Concern).

Page 37
Test Your Knowledge

1 a) Peregrine falcon.
When diving towards the
ground, it can reach speeds
of over 200mph (320kph),
making it the fastest bird.
The cheetah is the fastest
land animal, and the black
marlin is the fastest fish.
2 c) Condor.
**3 b) An animal that sleeps
at night and is awake in
the day.** It's the opposite
of nocturnal.
4 True. Some species can also
regrow a new tail afterwards,
although it is usually shorter
than the original tail.

Page 38
Spreading Out Animals

Page 39
One of a Kind

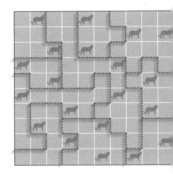

Page 40
Dig and Discover

1. **DODO**
2. **WOOLLY MAMMOTH**
3. **THYLACINE**
4. **WESTERN BLACK RHINO**
5. **GOLDEN TOAD**
6. **MYLODON** (also known as the giant ground sloth.)
7. **QUAGGA**
8. **SMILODON** (also known as the sabre-toothed tiger.)

Page 41
Fossil Hunt

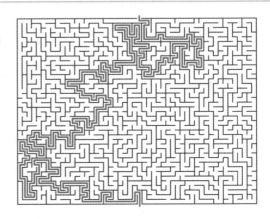

Page 45
The Open Ocean

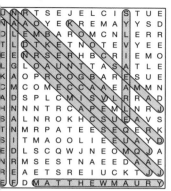

Page 46
A Kelp-ing Hand

Page 47
A Tall Tale

	2	3	1	3	2	
2	4	3	5	1	2	2
4	1	2	4	3	5	1
3	2	4	1	5	3	2
1	5	1	3	2	4	2
2	3	5	2	4	1	3
	2	1	4	2	3	

Pages 48-49
The World Ocean

ARCTIC OCEAN
ATLANTIC OCEAN
BALTIC SEA
BERING SEA
BLACK SEA
CASPIAN SEA
INDIAN OCEAN

8 MEDITERRANEAN SEA
9 NORTH SEA
10 PACIFIC OCEAN
11 SEA OF JAPAN
12 SEA OF OKHOTSK
13 SOUTH CHINA SEA
14 SOUTHERN OCEAN

Page 50
In A Spin

Page 51
Changing Directions

3	8	16	17	12
4	25	9	24	20
2	18	11	6	15
1	22	21	23	7
13	19	10	5	14

Page 53
Temperature Trouble

3	2	4	1	6	9	7	5	8
9	5	7	8	2	3	1	6	4
6	1	8	5	4	7	9	3	2
7	8	6	3	9	5	4	2	1
5	9	2	4	1	8	3	7	6
1	4	3	2	7	6	5	8	9
2	7	9	6	3	4	8	1	5
8	3	1	9	5	2	6	4	7
4	6	5	7	8	1	2	9	3

Page 54
Light Up the Deep

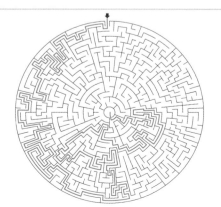

An example of an insect that uses bioluminescence is the firefly. Despite its name, it is actually a beetle.

Another insect is the glow-worm, which is actually a general name that refers to various different similar creatures that glow.

Page 52
Coral Reefs

Page 55
Quite a Catch

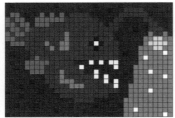

It's an anglerfish. Anglerfish use bioluminescence to lure prey towards them – and it has long, sharp teeth to eat it with!

Page 56
Deep-Sea Life

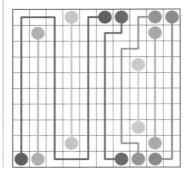

Page 57
Water Fun

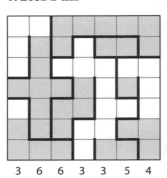

3 6 6 3 3 5 4

Page 58-59
Every Day's A Shoal Day

Page 60
A Mighty Mosaic
It's a shark fin!

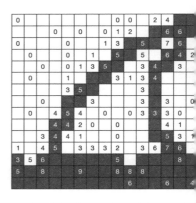

Page 61
Anemone, No Enemy

It's a clownfish. It has a mucus coating which protects it from the anemone's stinging tentacles.

Page 62
Go Fish

1. TUNA.
2. PARROTFISH.
3. SEAHORSE.
4. PUFFERFISH.
5. ANGLERFISH.
6. STONEFISH.
7. GOBLIN SHARK.
8. MUDSKIPPER.

Page 64
A Whale of a Time

This whale was approximately 81 years old.

Page 63
A Courtly Dance

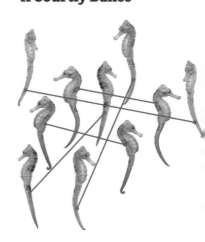

Page 65
Crack the Code

In the code, a dot represents a blip, and a dash represents a bleep. When you match the bleeps and blips to the code, you get the following message:

—•   ——   •—•   •——   •••   •—

This translates to, "Shall we have a swimming race?"

Page 66
Crustaceans

Crustacean Equations
1. It would require 16 shells.
2. 500 krill.
3. In this case, the giant isopod would be 50 times longer than the common woodlouse.

Page 67
Shellection Time

One of these shells spirals to the left, which is unusual. It's called a "sinistral" formation, and only about 10% of spiral shells grow this way.

Page 68
Hide and Sneak

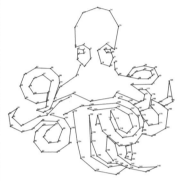

Page 69
Shady Sea-Creature

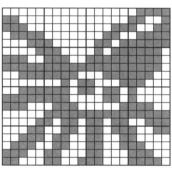

It's a giant squid.

Page 70
An Arm and a Leg

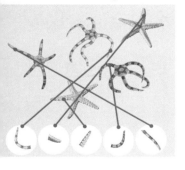

Page 71
Mind the Jellyfish!

Page 73
Spreading Pollution

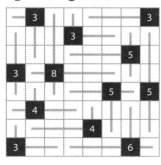

Page 74
Ocean Depths

EPIPLAGIC
Bottlenose dolphin.
Whale shark.
Portuguese man o'war.

MESOPELAGIC
Cuttlefish.
Giant squid.

BATHYPELAGIC
Anglerfish.
Vampire squid.

ABYSSOPELAGIC
Giant tube worm.

Page 75
Ocean Explorer Quiz

1. Cephalopods.
2. 500 miles (805km).
3. The goblin shark.
4. The Japanese spider crab.
5. Up to 50m (164ft).
6. The giant sea otter.
7. The Pacific Ocean.
8. The Denmark Strait Cataract.
9. Bioluminescence.
10. The whale shark.

Page 79
Outer Space

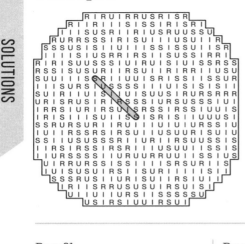

Page 80
Journey to the Centre

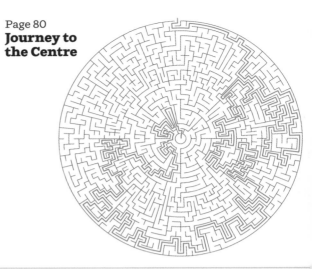

Page 81
The Big Bang

The curved lines make your brain think it is looking at a 3D tunnel heading away from you, so it bends the lines as if they were drawn along the sides of just such a tunnel. Because they are drawn straight on the page, this makes them look bent when your brain interprets them as following a curved surface.

Page 83
A Sizable Difference

From largest to smallest:
1. Jupiter.
2. Saturn.
3. Uranus.
4. Neptune.
5. Earth.
6. Venus.
7. Mars.
8. Mercury.

Page 85
A Layered Earth

From outside to centre:
1. CRUST
2. MANTLE
3. OUTER CORE
4. INNER CORE

Page 82
Colour and Uncover

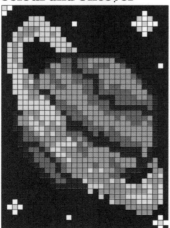

The pictures shows Saturn and its surrounding rings. Saturn's rings are the brightest, but Jupiter, Uranus and Neptune do have rings as well.

Page 84
The Blue Planet

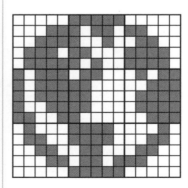

Page 86
Permission to Land

1				●	3		1
1	●	●	2	2	●	●	3
	3				3	●	●
1	●	2	●	1			3
	3		2		1	●	1
1	●	●		1		1	
		●	●			2	1
●	2	2	2		●	2	●

Page 87
Mathematical Mars

1. Olympus Mons is 25,000m (82,025ft) high.
2. It would take 11.3 months, i.e. about 11 months and 10 days.
3. 10.6 years. The 20 Earth years would take (365+365+365+366)x5 = 7,305 days, which can then be divided by 687.

Pages 88-89
The Night Sky

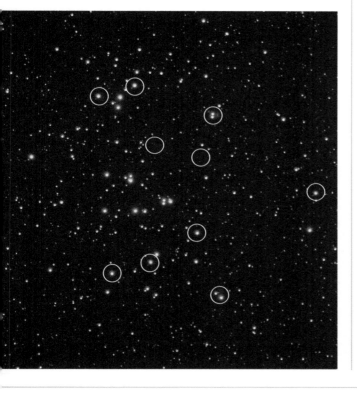

Page 90
Art in the Sky

This constellation is called Pisces and it is represented by two fish.

Page 91
It's a Sign

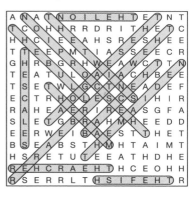

Page 92
Heating Up

2	6	7	5	3	8	9	1	4
4	9	5	7	1	2	3	8	6
1	3	8	4	9	6	7	5	2
9	8	2	3	5	1	4	6	7
6	1	4	9	8	7	5	2	3
7	5	3	2	6	4	1	9	8
8	4	6	1	7	5	2	3	9
5	7	9	8	2	3	6	4	1
3	2	1	6	4	9	8	7	5

Page 93
Solar Shadows
D.

Page 94
What Time Is It?
1. 10pm.
2. 10.30pm.
3. 11pm.
4. 6am the next day.

Page 95
Rise and Shine

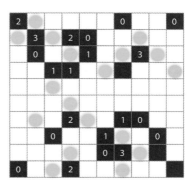

Page 98
Lunar Link

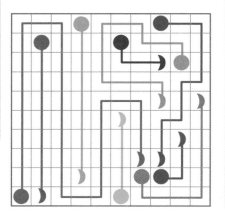

Page 99
Monochrome Moons

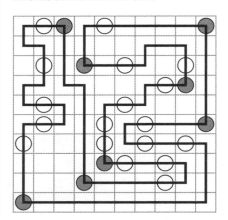

Pages 100-101
Asteroid Assignment

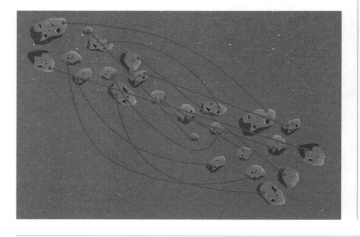

Page 104
Houston, We Have A Puzzle

A rocket.

Page 105
An Accidental Adventure

Page 106
Explorer's Quiz

1. The Milky Way.
2. Valentina Tereshkova.
3. Sirius, or Canis Majoris.
4. The mantle.
5. Jupiter.
6. A spacewalk.
7. Olympus Mons.
8. The northern lights.
9. Around 80.
10. 687 days.

Page 107
Moon Match

PLANETS	MOONS
EARTH	THE MOON
NEPTUNE	TRITON
	PROTEUS
SATURN	TITAN
	DIONE
	RHEA
JUPITER	GANYMEDE
	CALLISTO
	EUROPA
	IO

Page 111
Dig for Dinosaurs

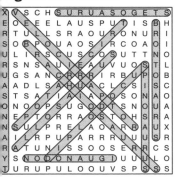

Pages 114-115
Pangea Puzzle

1 AFRICA
2 ANTARCTICA
3 AUSTRALIA
4 EURASIA
5 INDIA
6 NORTH AMERICA
7 SOUTH AMERICA

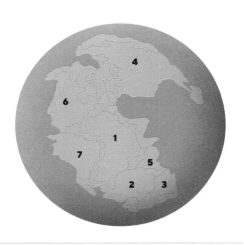

Page 112
Dinosaur Division

TRIASSIC	MUSSAURUS
	PLATEOSAURUS
	RIOJASAURUS
	STAURIKOSAURUS
JURASSIC	ALLOSAURUS
	ARCHAEOPTERYX
	DIPLODOCUS
	STEGOSAURUS
CRETACEOUS	ANKYLOSAURUS
	TRICERATOPS
	TYRANNOSAURUS REX
	VELOCIRAPTOR

Page 116
Fun with Fossils

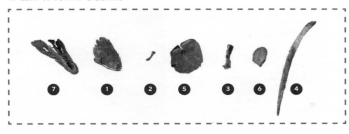

Page 113
Easy As TJC

	J	T		J	
J		C	T		T
T		T		C	J	J
T	T	C	J			J
C	C	J			T	T
T			T	J	C	
	C	J		J	C	

Page 117
Keep Out!

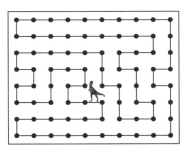

Pages 118-119
Pairs Of Prints

215

Page 120
Dinosaur Decisions

1. From smallest to largest, the order is:
Microraptor (40cm, 15in)
Stegosaurus (8.5m, 28ft)
Tyrannosaurus rex (12m, 39ft)
Spinosaurus (16m, 52ft)
Brachiosaurus (28m, 92ft)
2. 4 times.
3. 40. One Argentinosaurus weights the same as 20 African elephants.

Page 121
Size Assignment

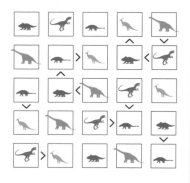

Page 122
Dino In Disguise

It's a *Tyrannosaurus rex*!

Page 123
Hidden Giant

The picture shows a *Diplodocus*, a plant-eating herbivore from the Jurassic Period.

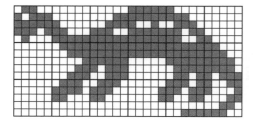

Pages 126-127
An Eggs-traordinary Find

Page 128
Herds and Hunting

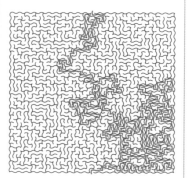

Page 129
Vicious Velociraptors

2	4			3		2	1
			5		5		
3			3		3		2
	2					3	
	3			1			2
3		3			1		3	
		3				4		2
	2						1

Dino Dot-to-dots

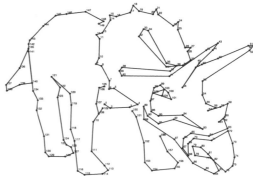

This dinosaur is a *Spinosaurus*. The spines on its back would have been joined together by skin to create a "sail", which might have been used to intimidate other dinosaurs.

This dinosaur is a *Triceratops*. The three horns on the top of its head were probably used defensively to help protect it from predators, such as *Tyrannosaurs*.

Page 132
Treasure Trove

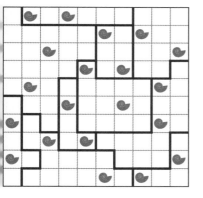

Page 133
A Pterrific Puzzle

It's a *Pterodactyl*. This flying reptile isn't technically a dinosaur, although they did live at the same time. It belongs to a group known as pterosaurs, which means "winged lizard".

Page 136
Missing Link Match
D.

Page 137
An Awesome Ancestor

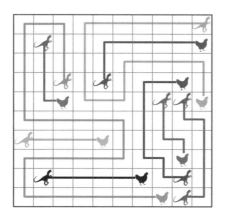

Pages 138-139
Dino Quiz

1. c) Three.
2. a) Palaeontologist.
3. b) Pangea. When it later split, the two halves were called Gondwana and Laurasia.
4. c) 8,800kg (8.6 tons).
5. b) *Brachiosaur.*
6. a) Australia.
7. c) Jurassic Coast.
8. a) *Velociraptor.*

Pages 142-143
What is Evolution?

CHARLES DARWIN	*Proposed the theory of evolution.*
WATSON AND CRICK	*Discovered the structure of DNA.*
MARY ANNING	*Made important fossil discoveries.*
MARIE CURIE	*Discovered radioactivity.*
ALEXANDER FLEMING	*Discovered the antibiotic penicillin.*
ISAAC NEWTON	*Discovered the laws of motion and gravity.*
ALAN TURING	*Developed core theories in computer science.*
EDWARD JENNER	*Developed the smallpox vaccine.*
GALILEO GALILEI	*Discovered the four main moons of Jupiter.*
STEPHEN HAWKING	*Predicted the existence of black holes.*
ALBERT EINSTEIN	*Developed the theory of relativity.*

Page 144
Dot-to-dot Discovery

This bird is a Galapagos finch, found on the Galapagos Islands in the Pacific Ocean. This group of different species are sometimes known as "Darwin's Finches".

Page 145
The Missing Link

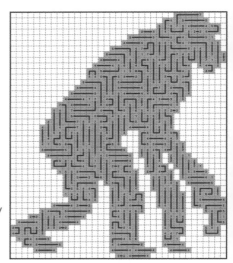

Animals of appearance somewhere between ape and human, such as this one, were part of the evolutionary journey from great ape to human.

Page 146
Odd Skull Out
C. It has a missing tooth.

Page 147
Land Bridges

Page 148
Sabre-Toothed Sweep

Page 150
A Cave of Colours

Page 151
The Hands-on Approach

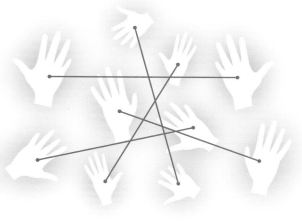

Page 152
Twisted Tongues

1. Hindi.
2. Arabic.
3. English.
4. Spanish.
5. Korean.
6. Mandarin.
7. Norwegian.
8. Portuguese.

Mandarin, a Chinese language, is the most widely-spoken language in the world.

Page 153
Writing on the Wall

The message reads: "Help, that mummy is waking up!"

Page 154
Pointed Pairs

Page 155
Stay Off My Land!

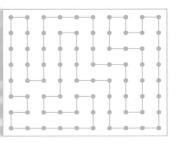

Page 156
Making Tracks

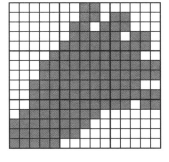

Page 157
A Tricky Trail

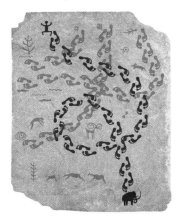

Page 159
An Artist's Expedition

Page 160
The Coded Secret

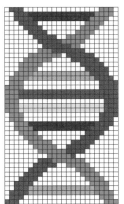

The picture shows a side-on view of part of a DNA molecule.

Page 161
Messaging Maths

1. 23 from each parent – and then they join up in pairs of matching chromosomes.
2. 30,000 genes.
3. 350 seconds, or 5 minutes 50 seconds. An actual marathon is 42.195km (26.2 miles) long, and the fastest marathon finishing time ever recorded was just over two hours.

Page 162
Skeleton Sorting

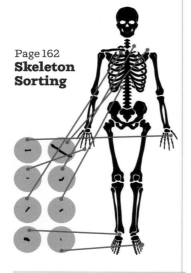

Page 163
Human Body Quiz

1. a) The femur, which is found in your thigh.
2. c) 32.
3. a) Iris.
4. b) Lungs – alveoli are tiny balloons that help transfer oxygen into the blood stream, and carbon dioxide back out of it.
5. b) 650, although it depends on how you count, since it's not always clear where the boundaries between muscles are.

Page 164
Parallel Puzzle

The red and purple lines are parallel, as are all of the lines. You can use a ruler to check this. Measure the distance between neighbouring lines on the left and on the right of the image – if they are the same, and the lines are both straight (which you can also check with the ruler), then they must be parallel!

Page 165
Mind-Bending Magic

The grid consists of perfect squares. They look like they are angled because your brain assumes that the dark blue circle segments line up – but because they don't line up, it makes the lines look bent instead.

Page 166
Viruses Versus Vaccines

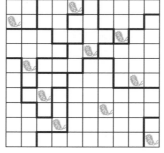

Page 167
Code-Breaking Conundrum

1	2	4	3	2	3	4	1
5	3	1	6	4	5	2	3
1	4	5	3	1	3	1	5
2	3	2	6	2	4	2	4
4	1	4	1	5	6	3	1
6	2	5	2	3	1	4	2
1	4	3	4	5	6	3	1
3	2	1	2	3	4	5	2

Page 168
Ready, Set, Science!

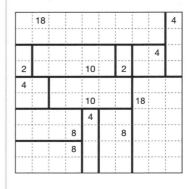

Page 169
Experimental Connections

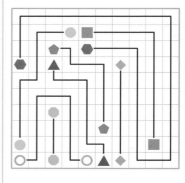

Pages 170-171
Evolved

1. b) Alexander Fleming.
2. a) Charles Darwin.
3. a) Flint.
4. c) Sabre-toothed tiger.
5. b) Argentina.
6. b) Food colouring.
7. a) *Lapis lazuli*.
8. c) Hieroglyphics.
9. a) 206.
10. a) Edward Jenner.

Pages 174-175
What is the Natural World?

PLANT FAMILY	FLOWER OR FOOD
APIACEAE	CELERY
LILIACEAE	LILY
ROSACEAE	ROSE
SOLANACEAE	POTATO
VIOLACEAE	VIOLET
FABACEAE	PEA
POACEAE	GRASS
LAURACEAE	AVOCADO
RUTACEAE	ORANGE
VITACEAE	GRAPE

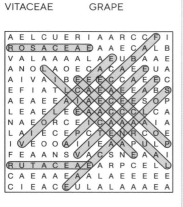

Page 176
Scaling New Heights

2 <	3 <	4 >	1	5
4	2 >	1	5	3
1	4 <	5 >	3 >	2
5	1 <	3	2	4
3	5	2	4	1

Page 177
Race to the Top

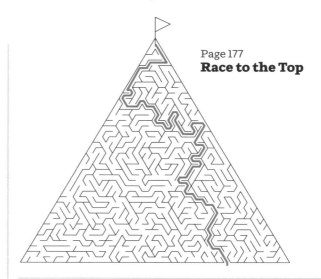

Page 178
Volatile Earth

Page 179
Jigsaw Plates

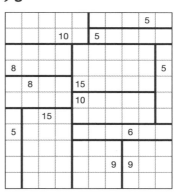

Page 180
Before and After

SOLUTIONS

Page 181
Island Map

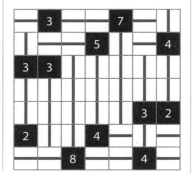

Page 182
Windy Weather

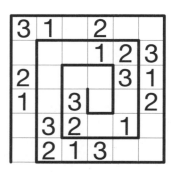

Page 183
Winds of the World

A = 4. CHINOOK
B = 7. PAMPERO
C = 6. MISTRAL
D = 1. BORA
E = 5. HARMATTAN
F = 3. BURAN
G = 2. BRICKFIELDER

Page 184
Firebreaks

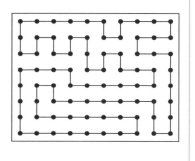

Page 186
The Water Cycle

Page 187
A Force of Nature

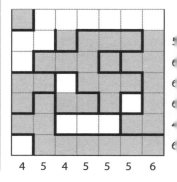

Page 185
Tornado Trouble

Pages 188-189
A Fool's Game

Page 190
Hidden Treasures

Page 191
What's Mine is Mine

Page 192
A Cunning Carnivore

The plant is a Venus flytrap. It lures flies into its traps and then snaps shut so that the flies can't escape! It then breaks them down into a juice that it can digest.

Page 193
Busy Bees

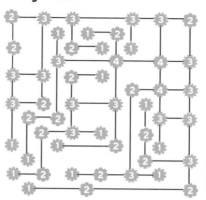

Page 197
Trees by the Numbers

1. It could grow 6.3m (21ft) in a week.
2. If 64 people stood on top of one another, they would reach to 384 feet (117m) – 4 feet (1.2m) taller than Hyperion.
3. 2831 BC.

Page 199
Fun Fungi

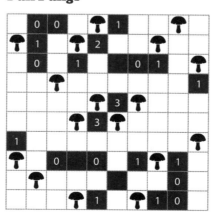

Page 195
Mixed-Up Meadow

1. ROSE
2. DAISY
3. TULIP
4. DAFFODIL
5. BLUEBELL
6. SNOWDROP
7. DANDELION
8. BUTTERCUP

Page 196
Ageing Arithmetic

A is the oldest tree.

Page 198
Microscopic Mushrooms

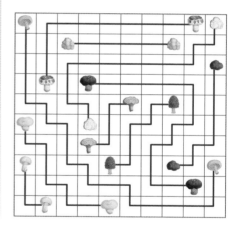

Pages 202-203
Natural World Quiz

1. a) Mount Everest.
2. b) Tectonic plates.
3. a) Australia.
4. c) Anemometer.
5. b) Fool's gold.
6. a) Angel Falls, Venezuela.
7. c) South Africa.
8. c) Photosynthesis.
9. b) Hyperion.
10. a) Fungi.

CREDITS

The publishers would like to thank the following sources for their kind permission to reproduce the pictures in this book.

All images © **NHM Images** except the following:

Alamy: 34TL

Getty Images: 12B, 13B, 37, 56BKG, 59T, 59B, 145

NASA: 76T

Shutterstock: 12T, 13T, 14-15, 18TL, 18C, 18BL, 21R, 22T, 24B, 25BC, 28-29BKG, 32-33B, 32C, 33R, 40C, 42T, 45, 46C, 48-49, 50B, 57B, 58-59BKG, 61R, 61B, 62C, 62B, 63, 65B, 67B, 70TL, 72, 75BL, 78C, 83, 84-85, 86-87, 88-89, 90-91, 92B, 93, 96-97, 98-99, 100-101, 102-103, 104-105, 106-107, 111, 113C, 114-115, 116BL, 118-119, 122, 124-125B, 126T, 127T, 128-129, 130T, 131T, 133, 134-135, 136, 138B, 140B, 143C, 147TR, 149, 151B, 153B, 154, 159B, 160-161, 162R, 163, 166-167, 172T, 174, 176-177, 179T, 180-181, 182-183, 184B, 185, 186-187, 188-189BKG, 190, 194, 195C, 196-197, 199BKG, 200-201B, 202L, 203BKG

Every effort has been made to acknowledge correctly and contact the source and/or copyright holder of each picture and Carlton Books Limited apologises for any unintentional errors or omissions that will be corrected in future editions of this book.